This Planner Belongs to

Name_____

Address_____

Phone Number_____

THE
WEIGHT-LOSS
DAY PLANNER

Publications International, Ltd.

Contributing Writer: Betsy A. Hornick, M.S., R.D., is a registered dietitian specializing in nutrition education and communications. She has written and edited numerous nutrition and health education publications for both consumers and health professionals, including materials published by the American Dietetic Association. She is a regular contributor to *Diabetic Cooking* magazine and a consultant for *Easy Home Cooking* magazine.

Illustrator: Roger Gorringe

The nutrient counter on pages 137–160 was adapted from: The U.S. Department of Agriculture, Agricultural Research Service. 2000. USDA Nutrient Database for Standard Reference, Release 16. Nutrient Data Laboratory Home Page, http://www.nal.usda.gov/fnic/foodcomp

Louis Weber, CEO
Publications International, Ltd.
7373 North Cicero Avenue
Lincolnwood, Illinois 60712

Permission is never granted for commercial purposes.

Manufactured in China.

8 7 6 5 4 3 2 1

ISBN: 1-4127-1016-2

Contents

Using This Planner

If you're serious about losing weight, the first order of business is to be conscious of what you eat. You can't make real changes in your diet, changes that will lead to long-term weight loss, if you don't watch what you're putting in your mouth. After all, during some part of every day—perhaps even the majority of every day!—most of us aren't concentrating on what we're eating. At the same time that we're eating, we're also working, talking, scurrying somewhere, supervising kids, reading, worrying, watching television, or being occupied by any number of other pursuits that distract us from our hands moving food to our mouths.

Lack of consciousness can also be self-protective. It's a way of hiding from reality. If you didn't consciously eat that bag of potato chips or that package of M&M's, you can't hold yourself accountable for them. But hiding can only hurt you and frustrate your weight-loss goals.

Being aware of every bite you eat means taking responsibility for what you consume. And that's the first step in altering your diet in a way that will produce weight loss.

> **If you're serious about losing weight, the first order of business is to be conscious of what you eat.**

getting started

So, begin to raise your food-awareness quotient by logging everything you eat in this planner. Each day of the week includes places for you to track the times you ate, what you ate, your location, your emotional state, and how hungry you were (on a scale of 1–5, with 1 being the least hungry). There's no question that emotions play a big role in when, where, and how much you eat. This food journal can help you identify how emotions affect your eating habits, and that's crucial to taking control.

Each day also has a convenient box for you to log your daily calorie intake as well as your intake of carbohydrate, protein, and fat and the amount of time you spent on exercise. At the end of each week, there's a box for you to enter your weight at week's end and the total

number of pounds you've lost. At the end of each month, there's a box to track how you're doing by recording your current measurements and those from when you began your diet, your beginning weight, your current weight, and the total number of pounds that you've lost.

It's important to fill in all the categories consistently. All these bits of information will help you discover and understand their impact on your eat-

> **Begin to raise your food-awareness quotient by logging everything you eat in this planner.**

WEEK ___5___

					Intake	
					Calories	1,150
DATE	September 15, 2004				Carbs	105
Time	Food(s)	Location	Emotional state	Hunger rating	Fat	35
8 a.m.	oatmeal & banana	work	calm	① ② ● ④ ⑤	Protein	93
12:30 p.m.	6 oz. yogurt	work	tense	① ● ③ ④ ⑤	**Activity (minutes)**	
1 p.m.	tuna salad	park	relaxed	① ② ● ④ ⑤		
	cherry tomatoes			① ② ③ ④ ⑤	Aerobic	20
	iced tea				Strengthening	0
4:00 p.m.	a few pretzels	work	on edge	① ● ③ ④ ⑤	Other	0
6:30 p.m.	chicken breast	home	calm	① ② ③ ● ⑤		
	salad, cookie					
8:30 p.m.	apple	home	steady	① ● ③ ④ ⑤		

ing patterns. They will also force you to spot your most significant downfalls. Is your diet filled with simple sugars (carbohydrates) that are high in calories and low in nutritional value? You'll know if you're keeping careful track of what foods you eat and the kind of nutrients in them.

> **Make sure to bring the planner with you everywhere to ensure accurate accounting.**

You can use the counter on pages 137–160 along with food labels to tally your daily intake of various nutrients and calories. If you see you're going overboard on high-calorie foods, you'll be able to cut back on them before you've packed on too many pounds. And you'll be able to substitute foods that are lower in calories and higher in vitamins, minerals, and fiber.

Make sure to bring the planner with you everywhere to ensure accurate accounting. Trying to recall what you ate hours later may lead to faulty reporting, especially when you conveniently forget snatching some of your child's french fries or popping a couple pieces of candy in your mouth while driving. After a few days of diligent logging, review your entries for patterns in your eating behaviors. You may be surprised by what you discover.

Remember, this planner is your best tool for successfully losing weight. But it's only as good as the information that gets recorded. Use it (the planner), *and* lose it (the weight)!

Weight-Loss Fundamentals

Losing weight isn't just a way to improve your appearance, though that may be your primary motivation for dieting. Taking off excess weight and learning a new way to eat is actually a long-term investment in your health—one with a pretty good rate of return.

In order to lose weight effectively and safely—and keep it off for good—you need to know something about nutrients in food and how they are used in the body. That's the case whether you follow one of the popular diet plans or take a more personalized approach and develop your own weight-loss plan.

Out of your control

In addition to calories, there are other factors that influence your weight. They are your age, your gender, and your genetic blueprint. Unfortunately, these factors are out of your control. So focus on decreasing your calorie intake and increasing your physical activity, the areas in which you *can* have an impact.

understanding calories

We all know that to lose weight we need to eat fewer calories. But it's hard to create a plan to eat fewer calories if we don't really understand what a calorie is or where exactly we get them from in our diet.

Basically, *calorie* is another word for energy. There are four sources of calories: the three energy-producing nutrients (carbohydrate, protein, and fat) and alcohol. Weight loss (and weight gain for that matter) is primarily an issue of calories: how many you consume and how many you expend. If the number of calories you eat and the number of calories you use (expend) each day are about the same, your weight will stay the same. It's only when you consume fewer calories than you use over a period of time that you will lose weight. And it's only when you eat more calories than you use that you will gain weight.

what's a pound worth?

Losing one pound comes down to this number: 3,500. There are 3,500 calories in one pound of body weight. That means you need to create a 3,500-calorie deficit to

Calorie counts

Here's where the calories you eat come from. All are nutrients except alcohol, which only provides calories.

1 gram of carbohydrate provides 4 calories
1 gram of protein provides 4 calories
1 gram of alcohol provides 7 calories
1 gram of fat provides 9 calories

lose just one pound. You can do that in one of three ways: eating 3,500 fewer calories, burning 3,500 more calories through physical activity, or combining physical activity with reducing your calorie intake for a total 3,500-calorie loss.

Of course, what's true for weight loss is also true for weight gain. Eat 3,500 more calories or burn 3,500 calories less through exercise (or a combination of both), and you will gain a pound.

While 3,500 may sound like a huge number of calories to consume, calories actually add up quickly. That's why it's so easy to gain weight.

Gaining a pound is as easy as eating an extra 250 calories a day (for instance, any of these: a medium bagel, three chocolate chip cookies, or two ounces cheddar cheese) for two weeks. It's also as easy as skipping a daily workout for two weeks without cutting back on your caloric intake.

nutrient fundamentals

A calorie is a calorie, no matter what kind of food it comes packaged in. Any calories eaten that your body doesn't burn for energy are stored as body fat. It's that simple.

But there is a difference between the primary energy-producing nutrients in terms of how many calories per gram they each provide. And that's important to know about when you're trying to lose weight.

carbohydrate. Carbohydrate, which includes sugars and starches, provides four calories per gram. It is the body's primary source of fuel and can be found in all plant foods, including fruits, vegetables, grains, and legumes. While some fault carbohydrate for the overweight epidemic in America, it really can't be blamed any more than fat can. The truth is, it's the refined carbohydrate, such as that found in processed baked goods and white rice, that packs on the pounds because we overeat them. And processed carbohydrate contributes little nutrition-ally; it's mostly empty calories. Complex carbo-hydrate, however, such as that found in whole grains, fruits, and vegetables, is

Fiber, the dieter's friend

Fiber is the indigestible part of plant foods. It's essential to good health, and it's a dieter's best friend. It provides no calories but it keeps you feeling full longer by sopping up fluid like a sponge and expanding in your stomach, which can help you stick to your diet.

A high-fiber, low-fat eating plan helps keep cholesterol levels down, which decreases your risk for colon cancer, and it helps regulate blood sugar so levels don't rise too quickly or too high after eating carbohydrate-rich meals.

Experts recommend that you consume about 20 to 35 grams of fiber every day, even if weight loss is not your goal. That's the amount of fiber that will help prevent disease. Remember, if you increase your intake of fiber, you also need to increase your fluid intake.

full of vitamins and minerals as well as fiber—a type of carbohydrate that fills you up but is calorie free because it is indigestible.

> **Fiber is a type of carbohydrate that fills you up but is calorie free because it is indigestible.**

protein. Protein, which is supplied by both animal and plant foods, is used to build, repair, and maintain your body's tissues, including muscles, skin, and internal organs. Like carbohydrate, protein provides four calories per gram, whether the source is of animal or plant origin. The crucial difference between animal and plant sources of protein for a dieter is that animal sources tend to contain more fat, including unhealthy saturated fat.

fat. Since fat has nine calories per gram, the highest number of all the sources of calories, it's especially important to be aware of how much fat you're taking in, no matter what its source. Fat is an essential component of every cell in your body; your body can't function without it. And it promotes healthy skin and partners with certain vitamins, carrying them to wherever your body needs them. Fat also plays an important role in satisfying hunger. But if you eat too much, you'll gain weight and raise your cholesterol levels, both of which are unhealthy.

alcohol. Alcohol is the fourth calorie source, but it is not a nutrient. It provides seven calories per gram, almost double that of carbohydrate and protein and close to the amount from fat. But alcohol provides no other nutritional benefits for its calories. So if you have a habit of drinking a beer or cocktail before dinner, cutting that out of your diet alone will help lead to weight loss.

water

You may not realize it, but water is a nutrient, too. It's essential to life. But unlike the other nutrients (carbohydrate, protein, and fat), it's calorie free. So it's not only important to drink it for your health, it can be a central part of your weight-loss plan.

Water helps regulate your body temperature, transports nutrients to your body cells, and carries waste products away. It also aids in digestion; moistens body tissues such as your eyes, mouth, and nose; and helps cushion your joints and protect your body organs and tissues.

Each day, your body loses about two to three quarts of water. Because of water's essential roles in your body, it's important to replace what you lose by drinking throughout the day. You can also obtain about three to four cups of fluid a day from foods, depending on your food choices.

Water is a plus for dieters because it's filling. That's especially true when your diet is rich in fiber, because fluid and fiber work together to provide a sense of fullness. Foods with a high water content have also been shown to help you feel more satisfied sooner.

Foods that are naturally rich in water include fruits, vegetables, low-fat milk, and cooked grains, as well as lean meats, poultry, fish, beans and water-rich dishes such as soups, stews, casseroles, pasta with vegetables, and fruit-based desserts.

> **Water is a plus for dieters because it's filling. That's especially true when your diet is rich in fiber.**

Getting Personal

When it comes to dieting, it's best to look before you leap. That means doing some serious self-assessment of your overall health, your current weight versus your optimum weight, your fitness level, and your weight-loss goals.

rate your weight

Before you can set a goal weight, you need to know about how much you should weigh. There are a couple different ways to figure that out.

You can get a quick assessment of your desirable weight by using your height. Although experts no longer recommend an "ideal" weight based on your height, you can get a general idea using this technique:

For women, allow 100 pounds for your first five feet of height. Add five pounds for every inch above that. (If you're under five feet, subtract four pounds for every inch under.) So, if you're five feet four inches tall, your desirable weight would be about 120 pounds.

For men, allow 106 pounds for your first five feet of height. Add six pounds for every inch over that. So if you're five feet nine inches tall, your desirable weight would be about 160 pounds.

Keep in mind that the suggested weight you get from this method may not be realistic for you. If you have a large bone structure, your desirable weight will be higher by about 10 percent. And if you have a small frame, your desirable weight may be about 10 percent lower. The amount of muscle you

> **Before you can set a goal weight, you need to know about how much you should weigh.**

have also impacts your weight because muscle weighs more than fat. Although the average dieter is rarely that muscular, if you do happen to work out a lot and have a lot of muscle, the number on the scale will be higher even though you look lean.

A more accurate assessment of your current weight can be obtained by determining your body mass index (BMI). This is a widely accepted measurement that can tell you whether your weight falls into a range that's optimal for health. It also indicates how much extra fat you are carrying around.

Here's how to determine your BMI:

1. Weigh yourself first thing in the morning.
2. Confirm your height, and convert it to inches.

(For instance, 5 feet 5 inches becomes 65 inches.)

3. Multiply your weight (in pounds) by 700.
4. Divide the result in #3 by your height in inches.
5. Divide the result in #4 by your height in inches. The number that you get is your BMI.

A BMI between 19 and 24.9 is considered to be in the healthy range, the one associated with the least risk of heart disease. A BMI of 25 to 29.9 indicates that you are overweight. If your BMI is 30 or greater, you are obese and have a much higher risk of serious illness such as high blood pressure, diabetes, and heart disease.

In addition to calculating your optimal weight range, it's also important to consider where you carry your extra weight and whether you have weight-related health

The BMI can tell you whether your weight falls into a range that's optimal for health.

problems. Guidelines from the National Institutes of Health advise you to measure your waist size and assess your current health status.

Losing weight is especially important if any of these descriptions fit you:

- Your BMI is 30 or greater
- Your BMI is 25 to 29.9 and you have two or more weight-related health problems
- Your waist circumference exceeds 40 inches (for men) or 35 inches (for women) and you have two or more weight-related health problems

If your BMI is in the upper 20s or your waist circumference is high but you don't have weight-related health problems, you can still benefit from losing some weight to prevent future health problems. Note: BMI doesn't apply to children, people over age 74, or conditioned athletes who weigh more because they're muscular.

setting goals

Now that you know where you stand weight-wise, you can begin to set some goals. First, be sure your goal is specific. You can have one main goal, to lose a certain amount of weight by a certain date, or you can set a series of smaller goals to make your ultimate goal seem less daunting. Just be sure the goal you set is attainable. Unrealistic weight-loss goals only set you up for failure.

Setting a goal is easier if you know your daily calorie needs.

Setting a goal is easier if you know your daily calorie needs. First figure out how many calories you need to maintain your current weight. Here's how:

1. Multiply your current weight by 10 (for women) or by 11 (for men).
2. Decide whether you are inactive (you mainly sit, drive a car, read, type, or do other low-intensity

Calories in perspective

Although you may be anxious to lose weight as rapidly as possible, be careful not to reduce your daily calorie intake so much that you jeopardize your health. Women should not take in less than 1,200 calories a day, while men should get no less than 1,800 calories a day. It's hard to get all the vitamins and minerals you need each day when you reduce your intake below these amounts. In fact, it's still difficult even at these calorie levels, so consider taking a daily multivitamin and mineral supplement. If you boost your physical activity level at the same time that you reduce calories, you'll be able to take in a healthy and more satisfying number of calories while still losing weight.

activities), moderately active (active throughout the day with very little sitting), or active (participate in active physical sports or have a labor-intensive job such as construction).

For an inactive lifestyle add 300 to the result in #1; for a moderately active lifestyle add 500, and for an active lifestyle add 700.

3. The result is the number of calories you need each day to maintain your current weight.

But you don't want to maintain your weight, you want to lose weight! If you want to lose one pound per week, subtract 500 from the result in #2. Taking in 500 calories less for a week (500×7) will result in a loss of 3,500 calories— or one pound. If you want to lose weight more gradually, or the number of calories you come up with after subtracting 500 is too few to be healthy or reasonable at this point, subtract fewer calories from your daily calorie allotment. For instance, to lose ½ pound a week, subtract 250 calories.

Another way to use the formula above is to determine the number of calories you need each day for your goal weight. You can then consume that number of calories, which will be fewer than the number you need to maintain your current weight. Say you weigh 150 pounds and your goal weight is 130. An inactive person of 150 pounds needs 1,800 calories a day, while an inactive person who weighs 130 pounds needs 1,600 calories a day. If you reduce your daily intake to 1,600 calories a day, you are consuming 200 calories less a day, or 1,400 calories less a week. With some calorie-burning activity added in, you'd lose about ½ pound a week.

How fit are you?

Before you can make a physical activity plan part of your weight-loss effort, you need to assess how fit you are. You probably have a fairly good idea already, but here's a simple test to gauge your aerobic ability, your strength, and your flexibility. For specifics on adding physical activity to your daily life, see The Exercise Advantage on page 25.

1. Aerobic Ability
    After walking up more than one flight of stairs I feel

    1   2   3   4   5

    no discomfort   short of breath

2. Strength
    After lifting and carrying heavy items, such as groceries or a small child, I feel

    1   2   3   4   5

    no discomfort   weak and tired

3. Flexibility
    When bending and stretching to make a bed or tie my shoes, I feel

    1   2   3   4   5

    no discomfort   uncomfortable

If your total score is 9 points or higher, your level of fitness could use some help. If your total score was less than 9 points, you're on the right track to fitness, but you can still benefit from increasing your daily physical activity.

Building a Weight-Loss Diet

When you begin to plan your diet, try to think about choosing a new way to eat rather than a short-term solution to dropping a few pounds. Most people who successfully lose weight make changes in their lifestyle and eating patterns along the way, and these changes become habits. That's the key to maintaining the weight loss.

A diet that promises short-term weight loss may be appealing as a quick fix, but it won't deliver lasting results. Not only that, but diets that help you lose weight fast are usually unhealthy if you stick with them for a long time.

Following a healthy, practical diet can be challenging, especially considering all the choices out there and all the conflicting advice. Just remember that diet plans have their unique personalities and characteristics, and so do you. The trick is finding one—or creating one— that feels comfortable.

> **Personalizing your diet gives you a distinct advantage in the weight-loss game.**

nutrient math

Creating your own weight-loss program instead of following the dictates of a ready-made plan isn't difficult at all. And personalizing your diet gives you a distinct advantage in the weight-loss game: Dieters who design their own plan are more likely to lose weight and keep it off. To get started, it's a good idea to calculate the approximate amounts of carbohydrate, protein, and fat you should be eating each day. The recommended percentages (called dietary reference intakes, or DRIs) are ranges of these three energy-producing nutrients established by the Food and Nutrition Board of the Institute of Medicine. They are the amounts of nutrients that meet daily nutritional needs while minimizing the risk of disease:

Carbohydrate: 45 to 65 percent of your total calories

Protein: 10 to 35 percent of your total calories

Fat: 20 to 35 percent of your total calories

In Getting Personal, you calculated the number of calories you require every day. Use that number in the formulas below to determine the number of calories you need from each of the three nutrients.

Carbohydrate

Your calorie total _____ x 0.45 = _____ calories from carbohydrate

Your calorie total _____ x 0.65 = _____ calories from carbohydrate

Next, divide your calories from carbohydrate by 4 calories/gram to figure a range of carbohydrate you should have each day: _____ to _____ grams of carbohydrate

Protein

Your calorie total _____ x 0.10 = _____ calories from protein

Your calorie total _____ x 0.35 = _____ calories from protein

Next, divide your calories from protein by 4 calories/gram to figure a range of protein you should have each day: _____ to _____ grams of protein

Fat

Your calorie total _____ x 0.20 = _____ calories from fat

Your calorie total _____ x 0.35 = _____calories from fat

Next, divide your calories from fat by 9 calories/gram to figure a range of fat you should have each day: _____to_____ grams of fat

translating calories into foods

As you can see from the recommended DRIs on the previous page, carbohydrate should be the foundation of your diet. But by carbohydrate we don't mean the empty, sugary products such as white bread, white rice, and cookies that we've come to associate most with that nutrient. When nutrition experts recommend that you get 45 to 65 percent of your calories from carbohydrate, they're talking about vegetables, fruits, and whole grains, such as whole-wheat bread, brown rice, and barley. These are low-calorie, high-volume foods that are loaded with vitamins, minerals, and phytonutrients (naturally occurring plant compounds that may help the body fight disease). They also provide fiber, which helps fill you up, lower blood cholesterol levels, and reduce your risk for cancer. When you eat fruits, vegetables, and whole grains, they take the place of foods that are higher in calories and lower in

Separating the good from the fad

Diets that promise quick, effortless weight loss are seldom effective over the long run. Fad diets may result in short-term weight loss, but they are often unrealistic and take the fun out of eating. It's probably a fad diet if it
- promotes or bans a specific food or food group
- promises incredible results
- blames specific nutrients or foods for weight problems
- presents rigid rules for eating
- relies on testimonials, anecdotal support, or unpublished studies

You're more likely to lose weight and keep it off when your weight-loss plan
- does not restrict calories to fewer than 1,200 a day
- includes foods from all of the food groups
- does not forbid any foods
- encourages lifelong healthful eating habits
- advocates regular physical activity

nutrients. Aim to get at least five servings of fruits and vegetables a day, though closer to nine servings is even better. And aim for at least six servings of grains per day, with at least half of them whole grain.

You may think of protein as coming primarily from meat products, but non-meat protein foods include dairy products, fish, eggs, nuts, and legumes. Protein foods can also be full of saturated fat, so be sure to opt for low-fat milk, yogurt, and cheese products and lean meat, poultry, and fish. New evidence suggests that the calcium and protein in dairy foods can help you reach your weight-loss goals. It seems that calcium aids the body in burning fat, while protein helps build and maintain muscle, which also helps you burn more calories.

getting a grip on portions

It's almost impossible to control your weight if you don't keep an eye on recommended serving sizes. What many people don't realize is that a serving, as listed on the label of a food product or accompanying various food guide pyramids, is not necessarily the amount you usually eat. What you actually eat is a *portion* of food, which may be bigger or smaller than a recommended serving size. Nor is a serving the amount that fills your plate, bowl, or cup.

Serving sizes are established so you can judge the overall amount of food recommended by a specific food guide. These are based on the total number of recommended servings per day. So if you eat a larger portion, this may count as more than one serving.

A serving, as listed on the label of a food product, is not necessarily the amount you usually eat.

(For example, a single serving of pasta is ½ cup, according to the USDA Food Guide Pyramid. A typical dinner portion, though, might be 1 or 1½ cups, which would be the equivalent to 3 servings of the 6 to 11 recommended daily servings.) What's important is the total number of servings you eat over the course of a day.

One of today's biggest challenges is controlling portion sizes. We have become conditioned to expect large portions of food, especially when eating out. We've all but lost the ability to gauge the amount of food that's enough. Regaining your perspective and control over portion size is one of the most successful dieting strategies.

When starting out on a weight-loss plan, one way to keep tabs on portion sizes is to weigh and measure your food. Although this may seem time-consuming and involved, it doesn't take long to become familiar enough with portion sizes to eyeball them instead of measuring. But for quick estimations, especially when you're out and about, here's a quick guide to eyeballing portions:

One of today's biggest challenges is controlling portion sizes.

½ cup cooked cereal, rice, pasta, or legumes: hockey puck

¾ cup dry cereal: a handful

1 cup raw vegetables or leafy greens: a woman's fist

2 tablespoons raisins: Ping-Pong ball

2 to 3 ounces cooked meat, fish, or chicken: deck of cards

⅓ cup nuts: small handful

1 teaspoon margarine: tip of thumb

2 tablespoons light salad dressing: Ping-Pong ball

managing meals

Mealtime management, including the timing of meals, the foods that make up your meals, and the size of your meals, is essential to your weight-loss plan. These factors all help you manage your hunger so you can manage your weight. Sometimes all it takes to get rid of extra pounds is better meal management along with some extra activity.

time it right. You're more likely to overeat when you undereat. Skipping meals, especially breakfast, can unleash your hunger and cause you to overeat at your next meal or give in to excessive between-meal snacking. In the end, you usually eat more calories than you would have if you'd eaten the meal you skipped. Your body is programmed to require food every three to four hours, so you're better off eating a regular progression of meals and snacks throughout the day.

balance your meals.

The foods and nutrients that compose your meals will determine how much you eat and how satisfied you will feel. A meal that's heavy on carbohydrates such as bread, pasta, and sweets may not supply enough long-lasting energy to get you through until your next meal. When you include protein and some fat with your carbohydrates, your meal or snack becomes more satisfying and will hold you over longer. This could mean adding grilled chicken to your pasta, for instance, or spreading peanut butter on your toast.

be size wise. The size of your meals obviously has an effect on your caloric intake. Eating one or two small meals and then a large evening meal can result in a higher total calorie intake than does eating four to six smaller meals.

The Exercise Advantage

Weight loss isn't just about diet. Regular exercise paired with a healthy, lower-calorie eating plan, will help you become a lean, fat-burning machine and drop pounds more quickly than if you relied on diet alone. And once you establish the exercise habit, including simply being more physical in your daily life, you'll be able to keep the weight off for good.

make an appointment with exercise

For most of us, the trick to fulfilling the exercise commitment is actually scheduling it into our lives. That's where this planner comes in. Each week, make many appointments with exercise—and then don't break them! Write in the times you have allotted for exercise and consider them to be carved in stone, just as you would a business meeting, a doctor's appointment, or dinner with a friend.

The planner also has a designated area every day for you to record the amount of time you've spent doing aerobic and strengthening (strength-training) exercises. After you've been working out for a couple weeks, look back over your records and analyze how you're doing. Are you keeping your exercise commitment? Scheduling—and keeping—your exer-

> **Regular exercise paired with a healthy, lower-calorie eating plan will help you become a lean, fat-burning machine.**

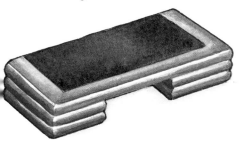

cise appointments will give you a sense of accomplishment because you will have met the goals you've set. After you review, take some time to plan ahead for the coming weeks, increasing the number of minutes you work out or the number of times a week you exercise. **goal setting.** Planning for exercise requires you to set some goals. That means you have to know how much weight you want to lose, how much time you will devote to exercise, and what that exercise will be.

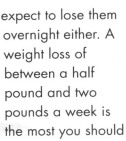

It's especially important to have realistic expectations. While it would be great to drop the extra pounds in a week, that's simply not feasible. You have to remember that you didn't put the extra pounds on overnight, so you can't

> The best exercise is the one that you will enjoy and stick with for the long haul.

expect to lose them overnight either. A weight loss of between a half pound and two pounds a week is the most you should aim for. If you try to lose more than that, you'll put your health at risk and lower your chances of keeping that weight off in the long run.

which exercise is best?

Frankly, the best exercise is the one that you will enjoy and stick with for the long haul—not just during the time you're trying to lose weight but for the rest of your life. Dieters who have lost weight and managed to keep it off for years maintain that exercise is the key to their success. But if you dislike the exercise you're doing—or if it's difficult to master or can only be done during certain times of the year or when the weather cooperates—it will be hard for you to make it a habit, even in the short run.

So, the first order of business when it comes to exercise is to choose an activity that gives you a lot of flexibility—or choose several activities that you can alternate. Find activities that you can do alone or with someone else, in good weather and bad. And pick exercise activities that don't require you to drive across town, buy loads of equipment, or overcommit yourself in terms of time or money.

There are two basic categories of exercise— aerobic and strength training—and your weight-loss efforts will be most enhanced if you incorporate both into your weekly exercise regimen.

aerobic exercise. Any form of exercise will help you burn extra calories, but aerobic exercises are especially good for fat burning. Aerobic exercises, such as walk-ing, running, swimming, and cycling, are those that work the large muscles— those in the legs and buttocks or arms and shoulders—continuously for an extended period of time. This kind of exercise increases your body's demand for oxygen, forcing your breathing and heart rate to speed up. And that's exactly what you want when you're trying to lose weight, because your body needs that extra oxygen to release stored body fat and use it as fuel for your working muscles. The longer you keep up the activity, the more

> **Choose an activity that gives you a lot of flexibility— or choose several activi-ties that you can alternate.**

stored body fat is released and burned as fuel.

Walking is the simplest and most versatile form of aerobic exercise. Almost everybody can do it, and it doesn't require a big investment in equipment. And it can be done outdoors or indoors, in virtually any location or locale, alone or with a friend, and in one chunk of time or in smaller increments when your schedule is tight. And you can adjust the intensity of your walking exercise to your current fitness level, adding speed, distance, time, and arm movements as you become more fit.

For cardiovascular fitness, you should exercise aerobically a minimum of three times a week. If you're really serious about losing body fat, however, shoot for five times a week or even every day. Build up to that frequency gradually, though, especially if you've been relatively inactive lately. Try to exercise in your target heart-rate zone (65 to 85 percent of your maximum heart rate) for a minimum of 20 minutes. Thirty minutes is a good goal to set for yourself, although if you can push that even further, to 40 or 50 or 60 minutes a day, you'll burn even more body fat.

For cardiovascular fitness, you should exercise aerobically a minimum of three times a week.

strength training. It's easy to overlook the benefits of strength training. After all, you can see how jogging or walking the treadmill can expend lots of calories and help you lose weight. But the benefits of strength training (also called weight training, weight lifting, and resistance training) aren't as obvious, even though they actually are even more plentiful.

Strength training builds muscles, and that increases your metabolism. That's because muscle is very active tissue, while fat tissue is not. The more muscle you have, the more calories you burn—even when you're lounging on the sofa or sitting at your desk! So, if you do at least two strength-training sessions a week, you really can burn more calories (and more body fat) during those times when your body isn't in motion. In fact, one study found that women who built muscle by strength training twice a week burned up to 300 more calories a day. Now there's an incentive to start a strength-training program!

In addition to burning calories at rest, strength training also gives you greater strength in performing everyday activities, such as carrying the groceries, and gives you an increased ability to do aerobic exercise. And it will strengthen your bones, give you a more toned, slim-looking physique and a better body composition (an improved ratio of lean tissue to fat), and protect you from injury.

Strength training requires the contraction of muscle against resistance. That resistance can be the weight of your own body (as when you do sit-ups or push-ups), a hand weight (also called a free weight or dumbbell), a resistance band (a long elastic loop), wrist and/or ankle weights (anchored to wrist or ankle with Velcro closures), or a weight machine (either at the gym or at home).

How do you know how much weight is appropriate for you? If you can

> **Women who built muscle by strength training twice a week burned up to 300 more calories a day.**

complete at least two sets of at least eight controlled repetitions with the weight you choose, then you are lifting the right amount of weight. If you can't, it's too heavy. However, if you can comfortably do more than three sets of 12 repetitions, it's time to move up to a heavier weight. You may need to use different weights for different exercises.

If you can comfortably do more than three sets of 12 repetitions, it's time to move to a heavier weight.

Your muscles will need a day of rest between strength-training sessions to repair and rebuild. But that doesn't mean you can't strength train every day if you want. You just need to work different muscle groups. So, if you want to do a strengthening workout every day, work your upper body one day and your lower body the next. However, if you prefer a complete day of rest from strength training, strength train your whole body at one session, then take the next day off.

The Starting Line

Date _____

My current weight _____

MY CURRENT MEASUREMENTS:

Chest	_____	inches
Upper arms	_____	inches
Waist	_____	inches
Hips	_____	inches
Thighs	_____	inches

MY CURRENT CLOTHING SIZES:

_____

_____

_____

HOW MUCH TIME AND HOW MANY DAYS I SPEND EVERY WEEK ON EXERCISE:

_____ minutes _____ days a week on aerobic exercise

_____ minutes _____ days a week on strength-training exercise

MY GOALS:

To lose _____ pounds

To do aerobic exercise _____ minutes _____ days a week

To do strength-training exercise _____ minutes _____ days a week

WEEK _____

DATE _____

Time	Food(s)	Location	Emotional state	Hunger rating
				① ② ③ ④ ⑤
				① ② ③ ④ ⑤
				① ② ③ ④ ⑤
				① ② ③ ④ ⑤
				① ② ③ ④ ⑤
				① ② ③ ④ ⑤
				① ② ③ ④ ⑤

Intake
Calories _____
Carbs _____
Fat _____
Protein _____
Activity (minutes)
Aerobic _____
Strengthening _____
Other _____

DATE _____

Time	Food(s)	Location	Emotional state	Hunger rating
				① ② ③ ④ ⑤
				① ② ③ ④ ⑤
				① ② ③ ④ ⑤
				① ② ③ ④ ⑤
				① ② ③ ④ ⑤
				① ② ③ ④ ⑤
				① ② ③ ④ ⑤

Intake
Calories _____
Carbs _____
Fat _____
Protein _____
Activity (minutes)
Aerobic _____
Strengthening _____
Other _____

DATE _____

Time	Food(s)	Location	Emotional state	Hunger rating
				① ② ③ ④ ⑤
				① ② ③ ④ ⑤
				① ② ③ ④ ⑤
				① ② ③ ④ ⑤
				① ② ③ ④ ⑤
				① ② ③ ④ ⑤
				① ② ③ ④ ⑤

Intake
Calories _____
Carbs _____
Fat _____
Protein _____
Activity (minutes)
Aerobic _____
Strengthening _____
Other _____

DATE _____

Time	Food(s)	Location	Emotional state	Hunger rating
				① ② ③ ④ ⑤
				① ② ③ ④ ⑤
				① ② ③ ④ ⑤
				① ② ③ ④ ⑤
				① ② ③ ④ ⑤
				① ② ③ ④ ⑤
				① ② ③ ④ ⑤

Intake
Calories _____
Carbs _____
Fat _____
Protein _____
Activity (minutes)
Aerobic _____
Strengthening _____
Other _____

MONTH _____ YEAR _____

Intake
Calories _____
Carbs _____
Fat _____
Protein _____

Activity (minutes)
Aerobic _____
Strengthening _____
Other _____

DATE _____

Time	Food(s)	Location	Emotional state	Hunger rating
				① ② ③ ④ ⑤
				① ② ③ ④ ⑤
				① ② ③ ④ ⑤
				① ② ③ ④ ⑤
				① ② ③ ④ ⑤
				① ② ③ ④ ⑤
				① ② ③ ④ ⑤

Intake
Calories _____
Carbs _____
Fat _____
Protein _____

Activity (minutes)
Aerobic _____
Strengthening _____
Other _____

DATE _____

Time	Food(s)	Location	Emotional state	Hunger rating
				① ② ③ ④ ⑤
				① ② ③ ④ ⑤
				① ② ③ ④ ⑤
				① ② ③ ④ ⑤
				① ② ③ ④ ⑤
				① ② ③ ④ ⑤
				① ② ③ ④ ⑤

Intake
Calories _____
Carbs _____
Fat _____
Protein _____

Activity (minutes)
Aerobic _____
Strengthening _____
Other _____

DATE _____

Time	Food(s)	Location	Emotional state	Hunger rating
				① ② ③ ④ ⑤
				① ② ③ ④ ⑤
				① ② ③ ④ ⑤
				① ② ③ ④ ⑤
				① ② ③ ④ ⑤
				① ② ③ ④ ⑤
				① ② ③ ④ ⑤

HOW AM I DOING?

Weekly Weight Check

_____ *pounds*
_____ *total lost*

TIP FOR THE WEEK

Eat breakfast! One study showed that people who skip breakfast have a 4 to 5 percent lower rate of metabolism than those who do not.

❏ DONE!

WEEK _____

DATE _____

Time	Food(s)	Location	Emotional state	Hunger rating
				① ② ③ ④ ⑤
				① ② ③ ④ ⑤
				① ② ③ ④ ⑤
				① ② ③ ④ ⑤
				① ② ③ ④ ⑤
				① ② ③ ④ ⑤
				① ② ③ ④ ⑤

Intake
Calories _____
Carbs _____
Fat _____
Protein _____
Activity (minutes)
Aerobic _____
Strengthening _____
Other _____

DATE _____

Time	Food(s)	Location	Emotional state	Hunger rating
				① ② ③ ④ ⑤
				① ② ③ ④ ⑤
				① ② ③ ④ ⑤
				① ② ③ ④ ⑤
				① ② ③ ④ ⑤
				① ② ③ ④ ⑤
				① ② ③ ④ ⑤

Intake
Calories _____
Carbs _____
Fat _____
Protein _____
Activity (minutes)
Aerobic _____
Strengthening _____
Other _____

DATE _____

Time	Food(s)	Location	Emotional state	Hunger rating
				① ② ③ ④ ⑤
				① ② ③ ④ ⑤
				① ② ③ ④ ⑤
				① ② ③ ④ ⑤
				① ② ③ ④ ⑤
				① ② ③ ④ ⑤
				① ② ③ ④ ⑤

Intake
Calories _____
Carbs _____
Fat _____
Protein _____
Activity (minutes)
Aerobic _____
Strengthening _____
Other _____

DATE _____

Time	Food(s)	Location	Emotional state	Hunger rating
				① ② ③ ④ ⑤
				① ② ③ ④ ⑤
				① ② ③ ④ ⑤
				① ② ③ ④ ⑤
				① ② ③ ④ ⑤
				① ② ③ ④ ⑤
				① ② ③ ④ ⑤

Intake
Calories _____
Carbs _____
Fat _____
Protein _____
Activity (minutes)
Aerobic _____
Strengthening _____
Other _____

MONTH _____ YEAR _____

Intake
Calories _____
Carbs _____
Fat _____
Protein _____
Activity (minutes)
Aerobic _____
Strengthening _____
Other _____

DATE _____

Time	Food(s)	Location	Emotional state	Hunger rating
				① ② ③ ④ ⑤
				① ② ③ ④ ⑤
				① ② ③ ④ ⑤
				① ② ③ ④ ⑤
				① ② ③ ④ ⑤
				① ② ③ ④ ⑤
				① ② ③ ④ ⑤

Intake
Calories _____
Carbs _____
Fat _____
Protein _____
Activity (minutes)
Aerobic _____
Strengthening _____
Other _____

DATE _____

Time	Food(s)	Location	Emotional state	Hunger rating
				① ② ③ ④ ⑤
				① ② ③ ④ ⑤
				① ② ③ ④ ⑤
				① ② ③ ④ ⑤
				① ② ③ ④ ⑤
				① ② ③ ④ ⑤
				① ② ③ ④ ⑤

Intake
Calories _____
Carbs _____
Fat _____
Protein _____
Activity (minutes)
Aerobic _____
Strengthening _____
Other _____

DATE _____

Time	Food(s)	Location	Emotional state	Hunger rating
				① ② ③ ④ ⑤
				① ② ③ ④ ⑤
				① ② ③ ④ ⑤
				① ② ③ ④ ⑤
				① ② ③ ④ ⑤
				① ② ③ ④ ⑤
				① ② ③ ④ ⑤

HOW AM I DOING?

Weekly Weight Check

_____ pounds
_____ total lost

TIP FOR THE WEEK

Make an appointment with exercise. Use your planner or a calendar to plot the times you will exercise during the week. Then be sure to show up on schedule and to be prepared, just as you would for an office meeting or a date with a friend.

☐ DONE!

WEEK _____

DATE _____

Time	Food(s)	Location	Emotional state	Hunger rating
				① ② ③ ④ ⑤
				① ② ③ ④ ⑤
				① ② ③ ④ ⑤
				① ② ③ ④ ⑤
				① ② ③ ④ ⑤
				① ② ③ ④ ⑤
				① ② ③ ④ ⑤

Intake
Calories _____
Carbs _____
Fat _____
Protein _____
Activity (minutes)
Aerobic _____
Strengthening _____
Other _____

DATE _____

Time	Food(s)	Location	Emotional state	Hunger rating
				① ② ③ ④ ⑤
				① ② ③ ④ ⑤
				① ② ③ ④ ⑤
				① ② ③ ④ ⑤
				① ② ③ ④ ⑤
				① ② ③ ④ ⑤
				① ② ③ ④ ⑤

Intake
Calories _____
Carbs _____
Fat _____
Protein _____
Activity (minutes)
Aerobic _____
Strengthening _____
Other _____

DATE _____

Time	Food(s)	Location	Emotional state	Hunger rating
				① ② ③ ④ ⑤
				① ② ③ ④ ⑤
				① ② ③ ④ ⑤
				① ② ③ ④ ⑤
				① ② ③ ④ ⑤
				① ② ③ ④ ⑤
				① ② ③ ④ ⑤

Intake
Calories _____
Carbs _____
Fat _____
Protein _____
Activity (minutes)
Aerobic _____
Strengthening _____
Other _____

DATE _____

Time	Food(s)	Location	Emotional state	Hunger rating
				① ② ③ ④ ⑤
				① ② ③ ④ ⑤
				① ② ③ ④ ⑤
				① ② ③ ④ ⑤
				① ② ③ ④ ⑤
				① ② ③ ④ ⑤
				① ② ③ ④ ⑤

Intake
Calories _____
Carbs _____
Fat _____
Protein _____
Activity (minutes)
Aerobic _____
Strengthening _____
Other _____

MONTH _____ YEAR _____

Intake
Calories _____
Carbs _____
Fat _____
Protein _____
Activity (minutes)
Aerobic _____
Strengthening _____
Other _____

DATE _____

Time	Food(s)	Location	Emotional state	Hunger rating
				① ② ③ ④ ⑤
				① ② ③ ④ ⑤
				① ② ③ ④ ⑤
				① ② ③ ④ ⑤
				① ② ③ ④ ⑤
				① ② ③ ④ ⑤
				① ② ③ ④ ⑤

Intake
Calories _____
Carbs _____
Fat _____
Protein _____
Activity (minutes)
Aerobic _____
Strengthening _____
Other _____

DATE _____

Time	Food(s)	Location	Emotional state	Hunger rating
				① ② ③ ④ ⑤
				① ② ③ ④ ⑤
				① ② ③ ④ ⑤
				① ② ③ ④ ⑤
				① ② ③ ④ ⑤
				① ② ③ ④ ⑤
				① ② ③ ④ ⑤

Intake
Calories _____
Carbs _____
Fat _____
Protein _____
Activity (minutes)
Aerobic _____
Strengthening _____
Other _____

DATE _____

Time	Food(s)	Location	Emotional state	Hunger rating
				① ② ③ ④ ⑤
				① ② ③ ④ ⑤
				① ② ③ ④ ⑤
				① ② ③ ④ ⑤
				① ② ③ ④ ⑤
				① ② ③ ④ ⑤
				① ② ③ ④ ⑤

HOW AM I DOING?

Weekly Weight Check

_____ pounds
_____ total lost

TIP FOR THE WEEK

Substitute complex carbs for simple-carb favorites and you won't feel deprived. Here are some suggestions: Instead of a plain bagel, try two slices of oat-bran bread. Instead of orange juice, have an orange. Instead of chips, have peanuts or almonds.

☐ DONE!

WEEK _____

DATE _____

Time	Food(s)	Location	Emotional state	Hunger rating
				① ② ③ ④ ⑤
				① ② ③ ④ ⑤
				① ② ③ ④ ⑤
				① ② ③ ④ ⑤
				① ② ③ ④ ⑤
				① ② ③ ④ ⑤
				① ② ③ ④ ⑤

Intake
Calories _____
Carbs _____
Fat _____
Protein _____
Activity (minutes)
Aerobic _____
Strengthening _____
Other _____

DATE _____

Time	Food(s)	Location	Emotional state	Hunger rating
				① ② ③ ④ ⑤
				① ② ③ ④ ⑤
				① ② ③ ④ ⑤
				① ② ③ ④ ⑤
				① ② ③ ④ ⑤
				① ② ③ ④ ⑤
				① ② ③ ④ ⑤

Intake
Calories _____
Carbs _____
Fat _____
Protein _____
Activity (minutes)
Aerobic _____
Strengthening _____
Other _____

DATE _____

Time	Food(s)	Location	Emotional state	Hunger rating
				① ② ③ ④ ⑤
				① ② ③ ④ ⑤
				① ② ③ ④ ⑤
				① ② ③ ④ ⑤
				① ② ③ ④ ⑤
				① ② ③ ④ ⑤
				① ② ③ ④ ⑤

Intake
Calories _____
Carbs _____
Fat _____
Protein _____
Activity (minutes)
Aerobic _____
Strengthening _____
Other _____

DATE _____

Time	Food(s)	Location	Emotional state	Hunger rating
				① ② ③ ④ ⑤
				① ② ③ ④ ⑤
				① ② ③ ④ ⑤
				① ② ③ ④ ⑤
				① ② ③ ④ ⑤
				① ② ③ ④ ⑤
				① ② ③ ④ ⑤

Intake
Calories _____
Carbs _____
Fat _____
Protein _____
Activity (minutes)
Aerobic _____
Strengthening _____
Other _____

MONTH _____ YEAR _____

Intake
Calories _____
Carbs _____
Fat _____
Protein _____

Activity (minutes)
Aerobic _____
Strengthening _____
Other _____

DATE _____

Time	Food(s)	Location	Emotional state	Hunger rating
				① ② ③ ④ ⑤
				① ② ③ ④ ⑤
				① ② ③ ④ ⑤
				① ② ③ ④ ⑤
				① ② ③ ④ ⑤
				① ② ③ ④ ⑤
				① ② ③ ④ ⑤

Intake
Calories _____
Carbs _____
Fat _____
Protein _____

Activity (minutes)
Aerobic _____
Strengthening _____
Other _____

DATE _____

Time	Food(s)	Location	Emotional state	Hunger rating
				① ② ③ ④ ⑤
				① ② ③ ④ ⑤
				① ② ③ ④ ⑤
				① ② ③ ④ ⑤
				① ② ③ ④ ⑤
				① ② ③ ④ ⑤
				① ② ③ ④ ⑤

Intake
Calories _____
Carbs _____
Fat _____
Protein _____

Activity (minutes)
Aerobic _____
Strengthening _____
Other _____

DATE _____

Time	Food(s)	Location	Emotional state	Hunger rating
				① ② ③ ④ ⑤
				① ② ③ ④ ⑤
				① ② ③ ④ ⑤
				① ② ③ ④ ⑤
				① ② ③ ④ ⑤
				① ② ③ ④ ⑤
				① ② ③ ④ ⑤

HOW AM I DOING?

MEASUREMENTS			WEIGHT		NOTES
	At diet's start	This month	Beginning weight	_____ pounds	_____
Chest	_____ inches	_____ inches	This month's weight	_____ pounds	_____
Upper arms	_____ inches	_____ inches	Total lost so far	_____ pounds	_____
Waist	_____ inches	_____ inches			_____
Hips	_____ inches	_____ inches			_____
Thighs	_____ inches	_____ inches			_____

WEEK _____

DATE _____

Time	Food(s)	Location	Emotional state	Hunger rating
				① ② ③ ④ ⑤
				① ② ③ ④ ⑤
				① ② ③ ④ ⑤
				① ② ③ ④ ⑤
				① ② ③ ④ ⑤
				① ② ③ ④ ⑤
				① ② ③ ④ ⑤

Intake
Calories _____
Carbs _____
Fat _____
Protein _____

Activity (minutes)
Aerobic _____
Strengthening _____
Other _____

DATE _____

Time	Food(s)	Location	Emotional state	Hunger rating
				① ② ③ ④ ⑤
				① ② ③ ④ ⑤
				① ② ③ ④ ⑤
				① ② ③ ④ ⑤
				① ② ③ ④ ⑤
				① ② ③ ④ ⑤
				① ② ③ ④ ⑤

Intake
Calories _____
Carbs _____
Fat _____
Protein _____

Activity (minutes)
Aerobic _____
Strengthening _____
Other _____

DATE _____

Time	Food(s)	Location	Emotional state	Hunger rating
				① ② ③ ④ ⑤
				① ② ③ ④ ⑤
				① ② ③ ④ ⑤
				① ② ③ ④ ⑤
				① ② ③ ④ ⑤
				① ② ③ ④ ⑤
				① ② ③ ④ ⑤

Intake
Calories _____
Carbs _____
Fat _____
Protein _____

Activity (minutes)
Aerobic _____
Strengthening _____
Other _____

DATE _____

Time	Food(s)	Location	Emotional state	Hunger rating
				① ② ③ ④ ⑤
				① ② ③ ④ ⑤
				① ② ③ ④ ⑤
				① ② ③ ④ ⑤
				① ② ③ ④ ⑤
				① ② ③ ④ ⑤
				① ② ③ ④ ⑤

Intake
Calories _____
Carbs _____
Fat _____
Protein _____

Activity (minutes)
Aerobic _____
Strengthening _____
Other _____

MONTH _____ YEAR _____

Intake
Calories _____
Carbs _____
Fat _____
Protein _____

Activity (minutes)
Aerobic _____
Strengthening _____
Other _____

DATE _____

Time	Food(s)	Location	Emotional state	Hunger rating
				① ② ③ ④ ⑤
				① ② ③ ④ ⑤
				① ② ③ ④ ⑤
				① ② ③ ④ ⑤
				① ② ③ ④ ⑤
				① ② ③ ④ ⑤
				① ② ③ ④ ⑤

Intake
Calories _____
Carbs _____
Fat _____
Protein _____

Activity (minutes)
Aerobic _____
Strengthening _____
Other _____

DATE _____

Time	Food(s)	Location	Emotional state	Hunger rating
				① ② ③ ④ ⑤
				① ② ③ ④ ⑤
				① ② ③ ④ ⑤
				① ② ③ ④ ⑤
				① ② ③ ④ ⑤
				① ② ③ ④ ⑤
				① ② ③ ④ ⑤

Intake
Calories _____
Carbs _____
Fat _____
Protein _____

Activity (minutes)
Aerobic _____
Strengthening _____
Other _____

DATE _____

Time	Food(s)	Location	Emotional state	Hunger rating
				① ② ③ ④ ⑤
				① ② ③ ④ ⑤
				① ② ③ ④ ⑤
				① ② ③ ④ ⑤
				① ② ③ ④ ⑤
				① ② ③ ④ ⑤
				① ② ③ ④ ⑤

HOW AM I DOING?

Weekly Weight Check

_____ pounds
_____ total lost

TIP FOR THE WEEK

Is precipitation, heat, or cold interfering with your daily exercise? Always have a backup activity for the days when you can't do your preferred exercise or when an exercise partner cancels.

❒ DONE!

D<small>ATE</small> _____

Time	Food(s)	Location	Emotional state	Hunger rating
				① ② ③ ④ ⑤
				① ② ③ ④ ⑤
				① ② ③ ④ ⑤
				① ② ③ ④ ⑤
				① ② ③ ④ ⑤
				① ② ③ ④ ⑤
				① ② ③ ④ ⑤

Intake
Calories _____
Carbs _____
Fat _____
Protein _____
Activity (minutes)
Aerobic _____
Strengthening _____
Other _____

D<small>ATE</small> _____

Time	Food(s)	Location	Emotional state	Hunger rating
				① ② ③ ④ ⑤
				① ② ③ ④ ⑤
				① ② ③ ④ ⑤
				① ② ③ ④ ⑤
				① ② ③ ④ ⑤
				① ② ③ ④ ⑤
				① ② ③ ④ ⑤

Intake
Calories _____
Carbs _____
Fat _____
Protein _____
Activity (minutes)
Aerobic _____
Strengthening _____
Other _____

D<small>ATE</small> _____

Time	Food(s)	Location	Emotional state	Hunger rating
				① ② ③ ④ ⑤
				① ② ③ ④ ⑤
				① ② ③ ④ ⑤
				① ② ③ ④ ⑤
				① ② ③ ④ ⑤
				① ② ③ ④ ⑤
				① ② ③ ④ ⑤

Intake
Calories _____
Carbs _____
Fat _____
Protein _____
Activity (minutes)
Aerobic _____
Strengthening _____
Other _____

D<small>ATE</small> _____

Time	Food(s)	Location	Emotional state	Hunger rating
				① ② ③ ④ ⑤
				① ② ③ ④ ⑤
				① ② ③ ④ ⑤
				① ② ③ ④ ⑤
				① ② ③ ④ ⑤
				① ② ③ ④ ⑤
				① ② ③ ④ ⑤

Intake
Calories _____
Carbs _____
Fat _____
Protein _____
Activity (minutes)
Aerobic _____
Strengthening _____
Other _____

MONTH _____ YEAR _____

Intake
Calories _____
Carbs _____
Fat _____
Protein _____

Activity (minutes)
Aerobic _____
Strengthening _____
Other _____

DATE _____

Time	Food(s)	Location	Emotional state	Hunger rating
				① ② ③ ④ ⑤
				① ② ③ ④ ⑤
				① ② ③ ④ ⑤
				① ② ③ ④ ⑤
				① ② ③ ④ ⑤
				① ② ③ ④ ⑤
				① ② ③ ④ ⑤

Intake
Calories _____
Carbs _____
Fat _____
Protein _____

Activity (minutes)
Aerobic _____
Strengthening _____
Other _____

DATE _____

Time	Food(s)	Location	Emotional state	Hunger rating
				① ② ③ ④ ⑤
				① ② ③ ④ ⑤
				① ② ③ ④ ⑤
				① ② ③ ④ ⑤
				① ② ③ ④ ⑤
				① ② ③ ④ ⑤
				① ② ③ ④ ⑤

Intake
Calories _____
Carbs _____
Fat _____
Protein _____

Activity (minutes)
Aerobic _____
Strengthening _____
Other _____

DATE _____

Time	Food(s)	Location	Emotional state	Hunger rating
				① ② ③ ④ ⑤
				① ② ③ ④ ⑤
				① ② ③ ④ ⑤
				① ② ③ ④ ⑤
				① ② ③ ④ ⑤
				① ② ③ ④ ⑤
				① ② ③ ④ ⑤

HOW AM I DOING?

Weekly Weight Check

_____ pounds

_____ total lost

TIP FOR THE WEEK

Today I am inspired to go beyond the boundaries of my weaknesses, to challenge the walls of my limitations, and to believe in endless possibilities.

❑ DONE!

WEEK _____

DATE _____

Time	Food(s)	Location	Emotional state	Hunger rating
				① ② ③ ④ ⑤
				① ② ③ ④ ⑤
				① ② ③ ④ ⑤
				① ② ③ ④ ⑤
				① ② ③ ④ ⑤
				① ② ③ ④ ⑤
				① ② ③ ④ ⑤

Intake
Calories _____
Carbs _____
Fat _____
Protein _____
Activity (minutes)
Aerobic _____
Strengthening _____
Other _____

DATE _____

Time	Food(s)	Location	Emotional state	Hunger rating
				① ② ③ ④ ⑤
				① ② ③ ④ ⑤
				① ② ③ ④ ⑤
				① ② ③ ④ ⑤
				① ② ③ ④ ⑤
				① ② ③ ④ ⑤
				① ② ③ ④ ⑤

Intake
Calories _____
Carbs _____
Fat _____
Protein _____
Activity (minutes)
Aerobic _____
Strengthening _____
Other _____

DATE _____

Time	Food(s)	Location	Emotional state	Hunger rating
				① ② ③ ④ ⑤
				① ② ③ ④ ⑤
				① ② ③ ④ ⑤
				① ② ③ ④ ⑤
				① ② ③ ④ ⑤
				① ② ③ ④ ⑤
				① ② ③ ④ ⑤

Intake
Calories _____
Carbs _____
Fat _____
Protein _____
Activity (minutes)
Aerobic _____
Strengthening _____
Other _____

DATE _____

Time	Food(s)	Location	Emotional state	Hunger rating
				① ② ③ ④ ⑤
				① ② ③ ④ ⑤
				① ② ③ ④ ⑤
				① ② ③ ④ ⑤
				① ② ③ ④ ⑤
				① ② ③ ④ ⑤
				① ② ③ ④ ⑤

Intake
Calories _____
Carbs _____
Fat _____
Protein _____
Activity (minutes)
Aerobic _____
Strengthening _____
Other _____

MONTH _____ YEAR _____

Intake
Calories _____
Carbs _____
Fat _____
Protein _____

Activity (minutes)
Aerobic _____
Strengthening _____
Other _____

DATE _____

Time	Food(s)	Location	Emotional state	Hunger rating
				① ② ③ ④ ⑤
				① ② ③ ④ ⑤
				① ② ③ ④ ⑤
				① ② ③ ④ ⑤
				① ② ③ ④ ⑤
				① ② ③ ④ ⑤
				① ② ③ ④ ⑤

Intake
Calories _____
Carbs _____
Fat _____
Protein _____

Activity (minutes)
Aerobic _____
Strengthening _____
Other _____

DATE _____

Time	Food(s)	Location	Emotional state	Hunger rating
				① ② ③ ④ ⑤
				① ② ③ ④ ⑤
				① ② ③ ④ ⑤
				① ② ③ ④ ⑤
				① ② ③ ④ ⑤
				① ② ③ ④ ⑤

Intake
Calories _____
Carbs _____
Fat _____
Protein _____

Activity (minutes)
Aerobic _____
Strengthening _____
Other _____

DATE _____

Time	Food(s)	Location	Emotional state	Hunger rating
				① ② ③ ④ ⑤
				① ② ③ ④ ⑤
				① ② ③ ④ ⑤
				① ② ③ ④ ⑤
				① ② ③ ④ ⑤
				① ② ③ ④ ⑤
				① ② ③ ④ ⑤

HOW AM I DOING?

Weekly Weight Check

_____ pounds

_____ total lost

TIP FOR THE WEEK

Don't let yourself get so hungry that you'll eat anything. Before going out, eat a high-protein snack and drink a large glass of water. That way, you'll be able to resist the temptation at the mall, movie theater, or grocery store.

☐ DONE!

DATE _____

Time	Food(s)	Location	Emotional state	Hunger rating
				① ② ③ ④ ⑤
				① ② ③ ④ ⑤
				① ② ③ ④ ⑤
				① ② ③ ④ ⑤
				① ② ③ ④ ⑤
				① ② ③ ④ ⑤
				① ② ③ ④ ⑤

Intake
Calories _____
Carbs _____
Fat _____
Protein _____
Activity (minutes)
Aerobic _____
Strengthening _____
Other _____

DATE _____

Time	Food(s)	Location	Emotional state	Hunger rating
				① ② ③ ④ ⑤
				① ② ③ ④ ⑤
				① ② ③ ④ ⑤
				① ② ③ ④ ⑤
				① ② ③ ④ ⑤
				① ② ③ ④ ⑤
				① ② ③ ④ ⑤

Intake
Calories _____
Carbs _____
Fat _____
Protein _____
Activity (minutes)
Aerobic _____
Strengthening _____
Other _____

DATE _____

Time	Food(s)	Location	Emotional state	Hunger rating
				① ② ③ ④ ⑤
				① ② ③ ④ ⑤
				① ② ③ ④ ⑤
				① ② ③ ④ ⑤
				① ② ③ ④ ⑤
				① ② ③ ④ ⑤
				① ② ③ ④ ⑤

Intake
Calories _____
Carbs _____
Fat _____
Protein _____
Activity (minutes)
Aerobic _____
Strengthening _____
Other _____

DATE _____

Time	Food(s)	Location	Emotional state	Hunger rating
				① ② ③ ④ ⑤
				① ② ③ ④ ⑤
				① ② ③ ④ ⑤
				① ② ③ ④ ⑤
				① ② ③ ④ ⑤
				① ② ③ ④ ⑤
				① ② ③ ④ ⑤

Intake
Calories _____
Carbs _____
Fat _____
Protein _____
Activity (minutes)
Aerobic _____
Strengthening _____
Other _____

MONTH _____ YEAR _____

Intake

Calories _____

Carbs _____

Fat _____

Protein _____

Activity (minutes)

Aerobic _____

Strengthening _____

Other _____

DATE _____

Time	Food(s)	Location	Emotional state	Hunger rating
				① ② ③ ④ ⑤
				① ② ③ ④ ⑤
				① ② ③ ④ ⑤
				① ② ③ ④ ⑤
				① ② ③ ④ ⑤
				① ② ③ ④ ⑤
				① ② ③ ④ ⑤

Intake

Calories _____

Carbs _____

Fat _____

Protein _____

Activity (minutes)

Aerobic _____

Strengthening _____

Other _____

DATE _____

Time	Food(s)	Location	Emotional state	Hunger rating
				① ② ③ ④ ⑤
				① ② ③ ④ ⑤
				① ② ③ ④ ⑤
				① ② ③ ④ ⑤
				① ② ③ ④ ⑤
				① ② ③ ④ ⑤
				① ② ③ ④ ⑤

Intake

Calories _____

Carbs _____

Fat _____

Protein _____

Activity (minutes)

Aerobic _____

Strengthening _____

Other _____

DATE _____

Time	Food(s)	Location	Emotional state	Hunger rating
				① ② ③ ④ ⑤
				① ② ③ ④ ⑤
				① ② ③ ④ ⑤
				① ② ③ ④ ⑤
				① ② ③ ④ ⑤
				① ② ③ ④ ⑤
				① ② ③ ④ ⑤

HOW AM I DOING?

MEASUREMENTS			WEIGHT		NOTES
	At diet's start	This month			
Chest	_____ inches	_____ inches	Beginning weight	_____ pounds	_____
Upper arms	_____ inches	_____ inches	This month's weight	_____ pounds	_____
Waist	_____ inches	_____ inches	Total lost so far	_____ pounds	_____
Hips	_____ inches	_____ inches			_____
Thighs	_____ inches	_____ inches			_____
					_____
					_____

WEEK _____

DATE _____

Time	Food(s)	Location	Emotional state	Hunger rating
				① ② ③ ④ ⑤
				① ② ③ ④ ⑤
				① ② ③ ④ ⑤
				① ② ③ ④ ⑤
				① ② ③ ④ ⑤
				① ② ③ ④ ⑤
				① ② ③ ④ ⑤

Intake
Calories _____
Carbs _____
Fat _____
Protein _____

Activity (minutes)
Aerobic _____
Strengthening _____
Other _____

DATE _____

Time	Food(s)	Location	Emotional state	Hunger rating
				① ② ③ ④ ⑤
				① ② ③ ④ ⑤
				① ② ③ ④ ⑤
				① ② ③ ④ ⑤
				① ② ③ ④ ⑤
				① ② ③ ④ ⑤
				① ② ③ ④ ⑤

Intake
Calories _____
Carbs _____
Fat _____
Protein _____

Activity (minutes)
Aerobic _____
Strengthening _____
Other _____

DATE _____

Time	Food(s)	Location	Emotional state	Hunger rating
				① ② ③ ④ ⑤
				① ② ③ ④ ⑤
				① ② ③ ④ ⑤
				① ② ③ ④ ⑤
				① ② ③ ④ ⑤
				① ② ③ ④ ⑤
				① ② ③ ④ ⑤

Intake
Calories _____
Carbs _____
Fat _____
Protein _____

Activity (minutes)
Aerobic _____
Strengthening _____
Other _____

DATE _____

Time	Food(s)	Location	Emotional state	Hunger rating
				① ② ③ ④ ⑤
				① ② ③ ④ ⑤
				① ② ③ ④ ⑤
				① ② ③ ④ ⑤
				① ② ③ ④ ⑤
				① ② ③ ④ ⑤
				① ② ③ ④ ⑤

Intake
Calories _____
Carbs _____
Fat _____
Protein _____

Activity (minutes)
Aerobic _____
Strengthening _____
Other _____

MONTH _____ YEAR _____

Intake
Calories _____
Carbs _____
Fat _____
Protein _____
Activity (minutes)
Aerobic _____
Strengthening _____
Other _____

DATE _____

Time	Food(s)	Location	Emotional state	Hunger rating
				① ② ③ ④ ⑤
				① ② ③ ④ ⑤
				① ② ③ ④ ⑤
				① ② ③ ④ ⑤
				① ② ③ ④ ⑤
				① ② ③ ④ ⑤
				① ② ③ ④ ⑤

Intake
Calories _____
Carbs _____
Fat _____
Protein _____
Activity (minutes)
Aerobic _____
Strengthening _____
Other _____

DATE _____

Time	Food(s)	Location	Emotional state	Hunger rating
				① ② ③ ④ ⑤
				① ② ③ ④ ⑤
				① ② ③ ④ ⑤
				① ② ③ ④ ⑤
				① ② ③ ④ ⑤
				① ② ③ ④ ⑤
				① ② ③ ④ ⑤

Intake
Calories _____
Carbs _____
Fat _____
Protein _____
Activity (minutes)
Aerobic _____
Strengthening _____
Other _____

DATE _____

Time	Food(s)	Location	Emotional state	Hunger rating
				① ② ③ ④ ⑤
				① ② ③ ④ ⑤
				① ② ③ ④ ⑤
				① ② ③ ④ ⑤
				① ② ③ ④ ⑤
				① ② ③ ④ ⑤
				① ② ③ ④ ⑤

How Am I Doing?

Weekly Weight Check

_____ pounds
_____ total lost

TIP FOR THE WEEK

At the end of the month, look over your food diary. Is there a trend toward eating larger portions or more snack foods? Applaud your successes but also notice where you can improve, and make that your goal for next month.

☐ DONE!

WEEK _____

Time	Food(s)	Location	Emotional state	Hunger rating	Intake
				① ② ③ ④ ⑤	Calories _____
				① ② ③ ④ ⑤	Carbs _____
				① ② ③ ④ ⑤	Fat _____
				① ② ③ ④ ⑤	Protein _____
				① ② ③ ④ ⑤	**Activity (minutes)**
				① ② ③ ④ ⑤	Aerobic _____
				① ② ③ ④ ⑤	Strengthening _____
				① ② ③ ④ ⑤	Other _____

DATE _____

Time	Food(s)	Location	Emotional state	Hunger rating	Intake
				① ② ③ ④ ⑤	Calories _____
				① ② ③ ④ ⑤	Carbs _____
				① ② ③ ④ ⑤	Fat _____
				① ② ③ ④ ⑤	Protein _____
				① ② ③ ④ ⑤	**Activity (minutes)**
				① ② ③ ④ ⑤	Aerobic _____
				① ② ③ ④ ⑤	Strengthening _____
				① ② ③ ④ ⑤	Other _____

DATE _____

Time	Food(s)	Location	Emotional state	Hunger rating	Intake
				① ② ③ ④ ⑤	Calories _____
				① ② ③ ④ ⑤	Carbs _____
				① ② ③ ④ ⑤	Fat _____
				① ② ③ ④ ⑤	Protein _____
				① ② ③ ④ ⑤	**Activity (minutes)**
				① ② ③ ④ ⑤	Aerobic _____
				① ② ③ ④ ⑤	Strengthening _____
				① ② ③ ④ ⑤	Other _____

DATE _____

Time	Food(s)	Location	Emotional state	Hunger rating	Intake
				① ② ③ ④ ⑤	Calories _____
				① ② ③ ④ ⑤	Carbs _____
				① ② ③ ④ ⑤	Fat _____
				① ② ③ ④ ⑤	Protein _____
				① ② ③ ④ ⑤	**Activity (minutes)**
				① ② ③ ④ ⑤	Aerobic _____
				① ② ③ ④ ⑤	Strengthening _____
				① ② ③ ④ ⑤	Other _____

MONTH _____ **YEAR** _____

Intake

Calories _____
Carbs _____
Fat _____
Protein _____

Activity (minutes)

Aerobic _____
Strengthening _____
Other _____

DATE _____

Time	Food(s)	Location	Emotional state	Hunger rating
				① ② ③ ④ ⑤
				① ② ③ ④ ⑤
				① ② ③ ④ ⑤
				① ② ③ ④ ⑤
				① ② ③ ④ ⑤
				① ② ③ ④ ⑤
				① ② ③ ④ ⑤

Intake

Calories _____
Carbs _____
Fat _____
Protein _____

Activity (minutes)

Aerobic _____
Strengthening _____
Other _____

DATE _____

Time	Food(s)	Location	Emotional state	Hunger rating
				① ② ③ ④ ⑤
				① ② ③ ④ ⑤
				① ② ③ ④ ⑤
				① ② ③ ④ ⑤
				① ② ③ ④ ⑤
				① ② ③ ④ ⑤
				① ② ③ ④ ⑤

Intake

Calories _____
Carbs _____
Fat _____
Protein _____

Activity (minutes)

Aerobic _____
Strengthening _____
Other _____

DATE _____

Time	Food(s)	Location	Emotional state	Hunger rating
				① ② ③ ④ ⑤
				① ② ③ ④ ⑤
				① ② ③ ④ ⑤
				① ② ③ ④ ⑤
				① ② ③ ④ ⑤
				① ② ③ ④ ⑤
				① ② ③ ④ ⑤

HOW AM I DOING?

Weekly Weight Check

_____ *pounds*
_____ *total lost*

TIP FOR THE WEEK

When dining out, ask the waiter to remove the bread basket or chips from your table. You can't fill up on fattening foods that aren't there!

☐ **DONE!**

WEEK _____

DATE _____

Time	Food(s)	Location	Emotional state	Hunger rating
				① ② ③ ④ ⑤
				① ② ③ ④ ⑤
				① ② ③ ④ ⑤
				① ② ③ ④ ⑤
				① ② ③ ④ ⑤
				① ② ③ ④ ⑤
				① ② ③ ④ ⑤

Intake

Calories _____
Carbs _____
Fat _____
Protein _____

Activity (minutes)

Aerobic _____
Strengthening _____
Other _____

DATE _____

Time	Food(s)	Location	Emotional state	Hunger rating
				① ② ③ ④ ⑤
				① ② ③ ④ ⑤
				① ② ③ ④ ⑤
				① ② ③ ④ ⑤
				① ② ③ ④ ⑤
				① ② ③ ④ ⑤
				① ② ③ ④ ⑤

Intake

Calories _____
Carbs _____
Fat _____
Protein _____

Activity (minutes)

Aerobic _____
Strengthening _____
Other _____

DATE _____

Time	Food(s)	Location	Emotional state	Hunger rating
				① ② ③ ④ ⑤
				① ② ③ ④ ⑤
				① ② ③ ④ ⑤
				① ② ③ ④ ⑤
				① ② ③ ④ ⑤
				① ② ③ ④ ⑤
				① ② ③ ④ ⑤

Intake

Calories _____
Carbs _____
Fat _____
Protein _____

Activity (minutes)

Aerobic _____
Strengthening _____
Other _____

DATE _____

Time	Food(s)	Location	Emotional state	Hunger rating
				① ② ③ ④ ⑤
				① ② ③ ④ ⑤
				① ② ③ ④ ⑤
				① ② ③ ④ ⑤
				① ② ③ ④ ⑤
				① ② ③ ④ ⑤
				① ② ③ ④ ⑤

Intake

Calories _____
Carbs _____
Fat _____
Protein _____

Activity (minutes)

Aerobic _____
Strengthening _____
Other _____

MONTH _____ YEAR _____

Intake
Calories _____
Carbs _____
Fat _____
Protein _____

Activity (minutes)
Aerobic _____
Strengthening _____
Other _____

DATE _____

Time	Food(s)	Location	Emotional state	Hunger rating
				① ② ③ ④ ⑤
				① ② ③ ④ ⑤
				① ② ③ ④ ⑤
				① ② ③ ④ ⑤
				① ② ③ ④ ⑤
				① ② ③ ④ ⑤
				① ② ③ ④ ⑤

Intake
Calories _____
Carbs _____
Fat _____
Protein _____

Activity (minutes)
Aerobic _____
Strengthening _____
Other _____

DATE _____

Time	Food(s)	Location	Emotional state	Hunger rating
				① ② ③ ④ ⑤
				① ② ③ ④ ⑤
				① ② ③ ④ ⑤
				① ② ③ ④ ⑤
				① ② ③ ④ ⑤
				① ② ③ ④ ⑤
				① ② ③ ④ ⑤

Intake
Calories _____
Carbs _____
Fat _____
Protein _____

Activity (minutes)
Aerobic _____
Strengthening _____
Other _____

DATE _____

Time	Food(s)	Location	Emotional state	Hunger rating
				① ② ③ ④ ⑤
				① ② ③ ④ ⑤
				① ② ③ ④ ⑤
				① ② ③ ④ ⑤
				① ② ③ ④ ⑤
				① ② ③ ④ ⑤
				① ② ③ ④ ⑤

HOW AM I DOING?

Weekly Weight Check

_____ pounds
_____ total lost

TIP FOR THE WEEK

Looking for a calorie freebie that will help squelch hunger pangs? Try eating foods that contain lots of fiber. Fiber is calorie free. Just be sure to increase your calorie-free fluid intake at the same time: Water or club soda does the trick!

❏ DONE!

DATE _____

Time	Food(s)	Location	Emotional state	Hunger rating
				① ② ③ ④ ⑤
				① ② ③ ④ ⑤
				① ② ③ ④ ⑤
				① ② ③ ④ ⑤
				① ② ③ ④ ⑤
				① ② ③ ④ ⑤
				① ② ③ ④ ⑤

Intake
Calories _____
Carbs _____
Fat _____
Protein _____

Activity (minutes)
Aerobic _____
Strengthening _____
Other _____

DATE _____

Time	Food(s)	Location	Emotional state	Hunger rating
				① ② ③ ④ ⑤
				① ② ③ ④ ⑤
				① ② ③ ④ ⑤
				① ② ③ ④ ⑤
				① ② ③ ④ ⑤
				① ② ③ ④ ⑤
				① ② ③ ④ ⑤

Intake
Calories _____
Carbs _____
Fat _____
Protein _____

Activity (minutes)
Aerobic _____
Strengthening _____
Other _____

DATE _____

Time	Food(s)	Location	Emotional state	Hunger rating
				① ② ③ ④ ⑤
				① ② ③ ④ ⑤
				① ② ③ ④ ⑤
				① ② ③ ④ ⑤
				① ② ③ ④ ⑤
				① ② ③ ④ ⑤
				① ② ③ ④ ⑤

Intake
Calories _____
Carbs _____
Fat _____
Protein _____

Activity (minutes)
Aerobic _____
Strengthening _____
Other _____

DATE _____

Time	Food(s)	Location	Emotional state	Hunger rating
				① ② ③ ④ ⑤
				① ② ③ ④ ⑤
				① ② ③ ④ ⑤
				① ② ③ ④ ⑤
				① ② ③ ④ ⑤
				① ② ③ ④ ⑤
				① ② ③ ④ ⑤

Intake
Calories _____
Carbs _____
Fat _____
Protein _____

Activity (minutes)
Aerobic _____
Strengthening _____
Other _____

MONTH _____ YEAR _____

Intake
Calories _____
Carbs _____
Fat _____
Protein _____

Activity (minutes)
Aerobic _____
Strengthening _____
Other _____

DATE _____

Time	Food(s)	Location	Emotional state	Hunger rating
				① ② ③ ④ ⑤
				① ② ③ ④ ⑤
				① ② ③ ④ ⑤
				① ② ③ ④ ⑤
				① ② ③ ④ ⑤
				① ② ③ ④ ⑤
				① ② ③ ④ ⑤

Intake
Calories _____
Carbs _____
Fat _____
Protein _____

Activity (minutes)
Aerobic _____
Strengthening _____
Other _____

DATE _____

Time	Food(s)	Location	Emotional state	Hunger rating
				① ② ③ ④ ⑤
				① ② ③ ④ ⑤
				① ② ③ ④ ⑤
				① ② ③ ④ ⑤
				① ② ③ ④ ⑤
				① ② ③ ④ ⑤
				① ② ③ ④ ⑤

Intake
Calories _____
Carbs _____
Fat _____
Protein _____

Activity (minutes)
Aerobic _____
Strengthening _____
Other _____

DATE _____

Time	Food(s)	Location	Emotional state	Hunger rating
				① ② ③ ④ ⑤
				① ② ③ ④ ⑤
				① ② ③ ④ ⑤
				① ② ③ ④ ⑤
				① ② ③ ④ ⑤
				① ② ③ ④ ⑤
				① ② ③ ④ ⑤

HOW AM I DOING?

MEASUREMENTS			WEIGHT		NOTES
	At diet's start	This month			
Chest	_____ inches	_____ inches	Beginning weight	_____ pounds	_____
Upper arms	_____ inches	_____ inches	This month's weight	_____ pounds	_____
Waist	_____ inches	_____ inches	Total lost so far	_____ pounds	_____
Hips	_____ inches	_____ inches			_____
Thighs	_____ inches	_____ inches			_____

WEEK _____

DATE _____

Time	Food(s)	Location	Emotional state	Hunger rating
				① ② ③ ④ ⑤
				① ② ③ ④ ⑤
				① ② ③ ④ ⑤
				① ② ③ ④ ⑤
				① ② ③ ④ ⑤
				① ② ③ ④ ⑤
				① ② ③ ④ ⑤

Intake

Calories _____
Carbs _____
Fat _____
Protein _____

Activity (minutes)

Aerobic _____
Strengthening _____
Other _____

DATE _____

Time	Food(s)	Location	Emotional state	Hunger rating
				① ② ③ ④ ⑤
				① ② ③ ④ ⑤
				① ② ③ ④ ⑤
				① ② ③ ④ ⑤
				① ② ③ ④ ⑤
				① ② ③ ④ ⑤
				① ② ③ ④ ⑤

Intake

Calories _____
Carbs _____
Fat _____
Protein _____

Activity (minutes)

Aerobic _____
Strengthening _____
Other _____

DATE _____

Time	Food(s)	Location	Emotional state	Hunger rating
				① ② ③ ④ ⑤
				① ② ③ ④ ⑤
				① ② ③ ④ ⑤
				① ② ③ ④ ⑤
				① ② ③ ④ ⑤
				① ② ③ ④ ⑤
				① ② ③ ④ ⑤

Intake

Calories _____
Carbs _____
Fat _____
Protein _____

Activity (minutes)

Aerobic _____
Strengthening _____
Other _____

DATE _____

Time	Food(s)	Location	Emotional state	Hunger rating
				① ② ③ ④ ⑤
				① ② ③ ④ ⑤
				① ② ③ ④ ⑤
				① ② ③ ④ ⑤
				① ② ③ ④ ⑤
				① ② ③ ④ ⑤
				① ② ③ ④ ⑤

Intake

Calories _____
Carbs _____
Fat _____
Protein _____

Activity (minutes)

Aerobic _____
Strengthening _____
Other _____

MONTH _____ YEAR _____

Intake

Calories _____
Carbs _____
Fat _____
Protein _____

Activity (minutes)

Aerobic _____
Strengthening _____
Other _____

DATE _____

Time	Food(s)	Location	Emotional state	Hunger rating
				① ② ③ ④ ⑤
				① ② ③ ④ ⑤
				① ② ③ ④ ⑤
				① ② ③ ④ ⑤
				① ② ③ ④ ⑤
				① ② ③ ④ ⑤
				① ② ③ ④ ⑤

Intake

Calories _____
Carbs _____
Fat _____
Protein _____

Activity (minutes)

Aerobic _____
Strengthening _____
Other _____

DATE _____

Time	Food(s)	Location	Emotional state	Hunger rating
				① ② ③ ④ ⑤
				① ② ③ ④ ⑤
				① ② ③ ④ ⑤
				① ② ③ ④ ⑤
				① ② ③ ④ ⑤
				① ② ③ ④ ⑤
				① ② ③ ④ ⑤

Intake

Calories _____
Carbs _____
Fat _____
Protein _____

Activity (minutes)

Aerobic _____
Strengthening _____
Other _____

DATE _____

Time	Food(s)	Location	Emotional state	Hunger rating
				① ② ③ ④ ⑤
				① ② ③ ④ ⑤
				① ② ③ ④ ⑤
				① ② ③ ④ ⑤
				① ② ③ ④ ⑤
				① ② ③ ④ ⑤
				① ② ③ ④ ⑤

HOW AM I DOING?

Weekly Weight Check

_____ pounds

_____ total lost

TIP FOR THE WEEK

Goals are better reached in small steps than in one giant leap.

❏ DONE!

WEEK _____

DATE _____

Time	Food(s)	Location	Emotional state	Hunger rating
				① ② ③ ④ ⑤
				① ② ③ ④ ⑤
				① ② ③ ④ ⑤
				① ② ③ ④ ⑤
				① ② ③ ④ ⑤
				① ② ③ ④ ⑤
				① ② ③ ④ ⑤

Intake
Calories _____
Carbs _____
Fat _____
Protein _____
Activity (minutes)
Aerobic _____
Strengthening _____
Other _____

DATE _____

Time	Food(s)	Location	Emotional state	Hunger rating
				① ② ③ ④ ⑤
				① ② ③ ④ ⑤
				① ② ③ ④ ⑤
				① ② ③ ④ ⑤
				① ② ③ ④ ⑤
				① ② ③ ④ ⑤
				① ② ③ ④ ⑤

Intake
Calories _____
Carbs _____
Fat _____
Protein _____
Activity (minutes)
Aerobic _____
Strengthening _____
Other _____

DATE _____

Time	Food(s)	Location	Emotional state	Hunger rating
				① ② ③ ④ ⑤
				① ② ③ ④ ⑤
				① ② ③ ④ ⑤
				① ② ③ ④ ⑤
				① ② ③ ④ ⑤
				① ② ③ ④ ⑤
				① ② ③ ④ ⑤

Intake
Calories _____
Carbs _____
Fat _____
Protein _____
Activity (minutes)
Aerobic _____
Strengthening _____
Other _____

DATE _____

Time	Food(s)	Location	Emotional state	Hunger rating
				① ② ③ ④ ⑤
				① ② ③ ④ ⑤
				① ② ③ ④ ⑤
				① ② ③ ④ ⑤
				① ② ③ ④ ⑤
				① ② ③ ④ ⑤
				① ② ③ ④ ⑤

Intake
Calories _____
Carbs _____
Fat _____
Protein _____
Activity (minutes)
Aerobic _____
Strengthening _____
Other _____

MONTH _____ YEAR _____

Intake
Calories _____
Carbs _____
Fat _____
Protein _____

Activity (minutes)
Aerobic _____
Strengthening _____
Other _____

DATE _____

Time	Food(s)	Location	Emotional state	Hunger rating
				① ② ③ ④ ⑤
				① ② ③ ④ ⑤
				① ② ③ ④ ⑤
				① ② ③ ④ ⑤
				① ② ③ ④ ⑤
				① ② ③ ④ ⑤
				① ② ③ ④ ⑤

Intake
Calories _____
Carbs _____
Fat _____
Protein _____

Activity (minutes)
Aerobic _____
Strengthening _____
Other _____

DATE _____

Time	Food(s)	Location	Emotional state	Hunger rating
				① ② ③ ④ ⑤
				① ② ③ ④ ⑤
				① ② ③ ④ ⑤
				① ② ③ ④ ⑤
				① ② ③ ④ ⑤
				① ② ③ ④ ⑤
				① ② ③ ④ ⑤

Intake
Calories _____
Carbs _____
Fat _____
Protein _____

Activity (minutes)
Aerobic _____
Strengthening _____
Other _____

DATE _____

Time	Food(s)	Location	Emotional state	Hunger rating
				① ② ③ ④ ⑤
				① ② ③ ④ ⑤
				① ② ③ ④ ⑤
				① ② ③ ④ ⑤
				① ② ③ ④ ⑤
				① ② ③ ④ ⑤
				① ② ③ ④ ⑤

HOW AM I DOING?

Weekly Weight Check

_____ pounds

_____ total lost

TIP FOR THE WEEK

Have a busy day ahead of you? You don't have to sacrifice exercise if you plan ahead. Just divide it into manageable chunks throughout the day. And if you can, make these shorter sessions more intense.

❑ DONE!

WEEK _____

DATE _____

Time	Food(s)	Location	Emotional state	Hunger rating
				① ② ③ ④ ⑤
				① ② ③ ④ ⑤
				① ② ③ ④ ⑤
				① ② ③ ④ ⑤
				① ② ③ ④ ⑤
				① ② ③ ④ ⑤
				① ② ③ ④ ⑤

Intake
Calories _____
Carbs _____
Fat _____
Protein _____
Activity (minutes)
Aerobic _____
Strengthening _____
Other _____

DATE _____

Time	Food(s)	Location	Emotional state	Hunger rating
				① ② ③ ④ ⑤
				① ② ③ ④ ⑤
				① ② ③ ④ ⑤
				① ② ③ ④ ⑤
				① ② ③ ④ ⑤
				① ② ③ ④ ⑤
				① ② ③ ④ ⑤

Intake
Calories _____
Carbs _____
Fat _____
Protein _____
Activity (minutes)
Aerobic _____
Strengthening _____
Other _____

DATE _____

Time	Food(s)	Location	Emotional state	Hunger rating
				① ② ③ ④ ⑤
				① ② ③ ④ ⑤
				① ② ③ ④ ⑤
				① ② ③ ④ ⑤
				① ② ③ ④ ⑤
				① ② ③ ④ ⑤
				① ② ③ ④ ⑤

Intake
Calories _____
Carbs _____
Fat _____
Protein _____
Activity (minutes)
Aerobic _____
Strengthening _____
Other _____

DATE _____

Time	Food(s)	Location	Emotional state	Hunger rating
				① ② ③ ④ ⑤
				① ② ③ ④ ⑤
				① ② ③ ④ ⑤
				① ② ③ ④ ⑤
				① ② ③ ④ ⑤
				① ② ③ ④ ⑤
				① ② ③ ④ ⑤

Intake
Calories _____
Carbs _____
Fat _____
Protein _____
Activity (minutes)
Aerobic _____
Strengthening _____
Other _____

MONTH _____ YEAR _____

Intake
Calories _____
Carbs _____
Fat _____
Protein _____
Activity (minutes)
Aerobic _____
Strengthening _____
Other _____

DATE _____

Time	Food(s)	Location	Emotional state	Hunger rating
				① ② ③ ④ ⑤
				① ② ③ ④ ⑤
				① ② ③ ④ ⑤
				① ② ③ ④ ⑤
				① ② ③ ④ ⑤
				① ② ③ ④ ⑤
				① ② ③ ④ ⑤

Intake
Calories _____
Carbs _____
Fat _____
Protein _____
Activity (minutes)
Aerobic _____
Strengthening _____
Other _____

DATE _____

Time	Food(s)	Location	Emotional state	Hunger rating
				① ② ③ ④ ⑤
				① ② ③ ④ ⑤
				① ② ③ ④ ⑤
				① ② ③ ④ ⑤
				① ② ③ ④ ⑤
				① ② ③ ④ ⑤
				① ② ③ ④ ⑤

Intake
Calories _____
Carbs _____
Fat _____
Protein _____
Activity (minutes)
Aerobic _____
Strengthening _____
Other _____

DATE _____

Time	Food(s)	Location	Emotional state	Hunger rating
				① ② ③ ④ ⑤
				① ② ③ ④ ⑤
				① ② ③ ④ ⑤
				① ② ③ ④ ⑤
				① ② ③ ④ ⑤
				① ② ③ ④ ⑤
				① ② ③ ④ ⑤

HOW AM I DOING?

Weekly Weight Check

_____ pounds

_____ total lost

TIP FOR THE WEEK

Start your meal with a bowl of soup or a salad (dressing on the side). These are low-calorie choices that are filling, helping you to eat smaller portions of higher-calorie entrées.

☐ DONE!

WEEK _____

DATE _____

Time	Food(s)	Location	Emotional state	Hunger rating
				① ② ③ ④ ⑤
				① ② ③ ④ ⑤
				① ② ③ ④ ⑤
				① ② ③ ④ ⑤
				① ② ③ ④ ⑤
				① ② ③ ④ ⑤
				① ② ③ ④ ⑤

Intake
Calories _____
Carbs _____
Fat _____
Protein _____
Activity (minutes)
Aerobic _____
Strengthening _____
Other _____

DATE _____

Time	Food(s)	Location	Emotional state	Hunger rating
				① ② ③ ④ ⑤
				① ② ③ ④ ⑤
				① ② ③ ④ ⑤
				① ② ③ ④ ⑤
				① ② ③ ④ ⑤
				① ② ③ ④ ⑤
				① ② ③ ④ ⑤

Intake
Calories _____
Carbs _____
Fat _____
Protein _____
Activity (minutes)
Aerobic _____
Strengthening _____
Other _____

DATE _____

Time	Food(s)	Location	Emotional state	Hunger rating
				① ② ③ ④ ⑤
				① ② ③ ④ ⑤
				① ② ③ ④ ⑤
				① ② ③ ④ ⑤
				① ② ③ ④ ⑤
				① ② ③ ④ ⑤
				① ② ③ ④ ⑤

Intake
Calories _____
Carbs _____
Fat _____
Protein _____
Activity (minutes)
Aerobic _____
Strengthening _____
Other _____

DATE _____

Time	Food(s)	Location	Emotional state	Hunger rating
				① ② ③ ④ ⑤
				① ② ③ ④ ⑤
				① ② ③ ④ ⑤
				① ② ③ ④ ⑤
				① ② ③ ④ ⑤
				① ② ③ ④ ⑤
				① ② ③ ④ ⑤

Intake
Calories _____
Carbs _____
Fat _____
Protein _____
Activity (minutes)
Aerobic _____
Strengthening _____
Other _____

MONTH _____ YEAR _____

Intake
Calories _____
Carbs _____
Fat _____
Protein _____

Activity (minutes)
Aerobic _____
Strengthening _____
Other _____

DATE _____

Time	Food(s)	Location	Emotional state	Hunger rating
				① ② ③ ④ ⑤
				① ② ③ ④ ⑤
				① ② ③ ④ ⑤
				① ② ③ ④ ⑤
				① ② ③ ④ ⑤
				① ② ③ ④ ⑤
				① ② ③ ④ ⑤

Intake
Calories _____
Carbs _____
Fat _____
Protein _____

Activity (minutes)
Aerobic _____
Strengthening _____
Other _____

DATE _____

Time	Food(s)	Location	Emotional state	Hunger rating
				① ② ③ ④ ⑤
				① ② ③ ④ ⑤
				① ② ③ ④ ⑤
				① ② ③ ④ ⑤
				① ② ③ ④ ⑤
				① ② ③ ④ ⑤
				① ② ③ ④ ⑤

Intake
Calories _____
Carbs _____
Fat _____
Protein _____

Activity (minutes)
Aerobic _____
Strengthening _____
Other _____

DATE _____

Time	Food(s)	Location	Emotional state	Hunger rating
				① ② ③ ④ ⑤
				① ② ③ ④ ⑤
				① ② ③ ④ ⑤
				① ② ③ ④ ⑤
				① ② ③ ④ ⑤
				① ② ③ ④ ⑤
				① ② ③ ④ ⑤

HOW AM I DOING?

MEASUREMENTS			WEIGHT	NOTES
	At diet's start	This month		
Chest	_____ inches	_____ inches	Beginning weight _____ pounds	_____
Upper arms	_____ inches	_____ inches	This month's weight _____ pounds	_____
Waist	_____ inches	_____ inches	Total lost so far _____ pounds	_____
Hips	_____ inches	_____ inches		_____
Thighs	_____ inches	_____ inches		_____
				_____

WEEK _____

DATE _____

Time	Food(s)	Location	Emotional state	Hunger rating
				① ② ③ ④ ⑤
				① ② ③ ④ ⑤
				① ② ③ ④ ⑤
				① ② ③ ④ ⑤
				① ② ③ ④ ⑤
				① ② ③ ④ ⑤
				① ② ③ ④ ⑤

Intake
Calories _____
Carbs _____
Fat _____
Protein _____

Activity (minutes)
Aerobic _____
Strengthening _____
Other _____

DATE _____

Time	Food(s)	Location	Emotional state	Hunger rating
				① ② ③ ④ ⑤
				① ② ③ ④ ⑤
				① ② ③ ④ ⑤
				① ② ③ ④ ⑤
				① ② ③ ④ ⑤
				① ② ③ ④ ⑤
				① ② ③ ④ ⑤

Intake
Calories _____
Carbs _____
Fat _____
Protein _____

Activity (minutes)
Aerobic _____
Strengthening _____
Other _____

DATE _____

Time	Food(s)	Location	Emotional state	Hunger rating
				① ② ③ ④ ⑤
				① ② ③ ④ ⑤
				① ② ③ ④ ⑤
				① ② ③ ④ ⑤
				① ② ③ ④ ⑤
				① ② ③ ④ ⑤
				① ② ③ ④ ⑤

Intake
Calories _____
Carbs _____
Fat _____
Protein _____

Activity (minutes)
Aerobic _____
Strengthening _____
Other _____

DATE _____

Time	Food(s)	Location	Emotional state	Hunger rating
				① ② ③ ④ ⑤
				① ② ③ ④ ⑤
				① ② ③ ④ ⑤
				① ② ③ ④ ⑤
				① ② ③ ④ ⑤
				① ② ③ ④ ⑤
				① ② ③ ④ ⑤

Intake
Calories _____
Carbs _____
Fat _____
Protein _____

Activity (minutes)
Aerobic _____
Strengthening _____
Other _____

MONTH _____ YEAR _____

Intake
Calories _____
Carbs _____
Fat _____
Protein _____

Activity (minutes)
Aerobic _____
Strengthening _____
Other _____

DATE _____

Time	Food(s)	Location	Emotional state	Hunger rating
				① ② ③ ④ ⑤
				① ② ③ ④ ⑤
				① ② ③ ④ ⑤
				① ② ③ ④ ⑤
				① ② ③ ④ ⑤
				① ② ③ ④ ⑤
				① ② ③ ④ ⑤

Intake
Calories _____
Carbs _____
Fat _____
Protein _____

Activity (minutes)
Aerobic _____
Strengthening _____
Other _____

DATE _____

Time	Food(s)	Location	Emotional state	Hunger rating
				① ② ③ ④ ⑤
				① ② ③ ④ ⑤
				① ② ③ ④ ⑤
				① ② ③ ④ ⑤
				① ② ③ ④ ⑤
				① ② ③ ④ ⑤
				① ② ③ ④ ⑤

Intake
Calories _____
Carbs _____
Fat _____
Protein _____

Activity (minutes)
Aerobic _____
Strengthening _____
Other _____

DATE _____

Time	Food(s)	Location	Emotional state	Hunger rating
				① ② ③ ④ ⑤
				① ② ③ ④ ⑤
				① ② ③ ④ ⑤
				① ② ③ ④ ⑤
				① ② ③ ④ ⑤
				① ② ③ ④ ⑤
				① ② ③ ④ ⑤

HOW AM I DOING?

Weekly Weight Check

_____ pounds

_____ total lost

TIP FOR THE WEEK

It takes 20 minutes for your brain to get the message that your stomach is full. So don't race through your meals. You'll eat less if your meals are eaten at a leisurely pace.

❑ DONE!

WEEK _____

DATE _____

Time	Food(s)	Location	Emotional state	Hunger rating
				① ② ③ ④ ⑤
				① ② ③ ④ ⑤
				① ② ③ ④ ⑤
				① ② ③ ④ ⑤
				① ② ③ ④ ⑤
				① ② ③ ④ ⑤
				① ② ③ ④ ⑤

Intake
Calories _____
Carbs _____
Fat _____
Protein _____
Activity (minutes)
Aerobic _____
Strengthening _____
Other _____

DATE _____

Time	Food(s)	Location	Emotional state	Hunger rating
				① ② ③ ④ ⑤
				① ② ③ ④ ⑤
				① ② ③ ④ ⑤
				① ② ③ ④ ⑤
				① ② ③ ④ ⑤
				① ② ③ ④ ⑤
				① ② ③ ④ ⑤

Intake
Calories _____
Carbs _____
Fat _____
Protein _____
Activity (minutes)
Aerobic _____
Strengthening _____
Other _____

DATE _____

Time	Food(s)	Location	Emotional state	Hunger rating
				① ② ③ ④ ⑤
				① ② ③ ④ ⑤
				① ② ③ ④ ⑤
				① ② ③ ④ ⑤
				① ② ③ ④ ⑤
				① ② ③ ④ ⑤
				① ② ③ ④ ⑤

Intake
Calories _____
Carbs _____
Fat _____
Protein _____
Activity (minutes)
Aerobic _____
Strengthening _____
Other _____

DATE _____

Time	Food(s)	Location	Emotional state	Hunger rating
				① ② ③ ④ ⑤
				① ② ③ ④ ⑤
				① ② ③ ④ ⑤
				① ② ③ ④ ⑤
				① ② ③ ④ ⑤
				① ② ③ ④ ⑤
				① ② ③ ④ ⑤

Intake
Calories _____
Carbs _____
Fat _____
Protein _____
Activity (minutes)
Aerobic _____
Strengthening _____
Other _____

MONTH _____ YEAR _____

Intake
Calories _____
Carbs _____
Fat _____
Protein _____
Activity (minutes)
Aerobic _____
Strengthening _____
Other _____

DATE _____

Time	Food(s)	Location	Emotional state	Hunger rating
				① ② ③ ④ ⑤
				① ② ③ ④ ⑤
				① ② ③ ④ ⑤
				① ② ③ ④ ⑤
				① ② ③ ④ ⑤
				① ② ③ ④ ⑤
				① ② ③ ④ ⑤

Intake
Calories _____
Carbs _____
Fat _____
Protein _____
Activity (minutes)
Aerobic _____
Strengthening _____
Other _____

DATE _____

Time	Food(s)	Location	Emotional state	Hunger rating
				① ② ③ ④ ⑤
				① ② ③ ④ ⑤
				① ② ③ ④ ⑤
				① ② ③ ④ ⑤
				① ② ③ ④ ⑤
				① ② ③ ④ ⑤
				① ② ③ ④ ⑤

Intake
Calories _____
Carbs _____
Fat _____
Protein _____
Activity (minutes)
Aerobic _____
Strengthening _____
Other _____

DATE _____

Time	Food(s)	Location	Emotional state	Hunger rating
				① ② ③ ④ ⑤
				① ② ③ ④ ⑤
				① ② ③ ④ ⑤
				① ② ③ ④ ⑤
				① ② ③ ④ ⑤
				① ② ③ ④ ⑤
				① ② ③ ④ ⑤

HOW AM I DOING?

Weekly Weight Check

_____ pounds

_____ total lost

TIP FOR THE WEEK

When you feel the urge to binge, drink some water. Water can curb the urge, and it can also stop you mid-binge. So, if you've momentarily lost your self-control, down a glass of water.

❑ DONE!

WEEK _____

DATE _____

Time	Food(s)	Location	Emotional state	Hunger rating
				① ② ③ ④ ⑤
				① ② ③ ④ ⑤
				① ② ③ ④ ⑤
				① ② ③ ④ ⑤
				① ② ③ ④ ⑤
				① ② ③ ④ ⑤
				① ② ③ ④ ⑤

Intake
Calories _____
Carbs _____
Fat _____
Protein _____
Activity (minutes)
Aerobic _____
Strengthening _____
Other _____

DATE _____

Time	Food(s)	Location	Emotional state	Hunger rating
				① ② ③ ④ ⑤
				① ② ③ ④ ⑤
				① ② ③ ④ ⑤
				① ② ③ ④ ⑤
				① ② ③ ④ ⑤
				① ② ③ ④ ⑤
				① ② ③ ④ ⑤

Intake
Calories _____
Carbs _____
Fat _____
Protein _____
Activity (minutes)
Aerobic _____
Strengthening _____
Other _____

DATE _____

Time	Food(s)	Location	Emotional state	Hunger rating
				① ② ③ ④ ⑤
				① ② ③ ④ ⑤
				① ② ③ ④ ⑤
				① ② ③ ④ ⑤
				① ② ③ ④ ⑤
				① ② ③ ④ ⑤
				① ② ③ ④ ⑤

Intake
Calories _____
Carbs _____
Fat _____
Protein _____
Activity (minutes)
Aerobic _____
Strengthening _____
Other _____

DATE _____

Time	Food(s)	Location	Emotional state	Hunger rating
				① ② ③ ④ ⑤
				① ② ③ ④ ⑤
				① ② ③ ④ ⑤
				① ② ③ ④ ⑤
				① ② ③ ④ ⑤
				① ② ③ ④ ⑤
				① ② ③ ④ ⑤

Intake
Calories _____
Carbs _____
Fat _____
Protein _____
Activity (minutes)
Aerobic _____
Strengthening _____
Other _____

Intake

Calories _____
Carbs _____
Fat _____
Protein _____

Activity (minutes)

Aerobic _____
Strengthening _____
Other _____

DATE _____

Time	Food(s)	Location	Emotional state	Hunger rating
				① ② ③ ④ ⑤
				① ② ③ ④ ⑤
				① ② ③ ④ ⑤
				① ② ③ ④ ⑤
				① ② ③ ④ ⑤
				① ② ③ ④ ⑤
				① ② ③ ④ ⑤

Intake

Calories _____
Carbs _____
Fat _____
Protein _____

Activity (minutes)

Aerobic _____
Strengthening _____
Other _____

DATE _____

Time	Food(s)	Location	Emotional state	Hunger rating
				① ② ③ ④ ⑤
				① ② ③ ④ ⑤
				① ② ③ ④ ⑤
				① ② ③ ④ ⑤
				① ② ③ ④ ⑤
				① ② ③ ④ ⑤
				① ② ③ ④ ⑤

Intake

Calories _____
Carbs _____
Fat _____
Protein _____

Activity (minutes)

Aerobic _____
Strengthening _____
Other _____

DATE _____

Time	Food(s)	Location	Emotional state	Hunger rating
				① ② ③ ④ ⑤
				① ② ③ ④ ⑤
				① ② ③ ④ ⑤
				① ② ③ ④ ⑤
				① ② ③ ④ ⑤
				① ② ③ ④ ⑤
				① ② ③ ④ ⑤

HOW AM I DOING?

Weekly Weight Check

_____ pounds
_____ total lost

TIP FOR THE WEEK

Some medications, including insulin and steroids, work against weight loss. If you're doing everything right but are still having trouble losing weight, check with your physician and pharmacist to see if there is a link between medicines you take on a regular basis and your weight.

❒ DONE!

DATE _____

Time	Food(s)	Location	Emotional state	Hunger rating
				① ② ③ ④ ⑤
				① ② ③ ④ ⑤
				① ② ③ ④ ⑤
				① ② ③ ④ ⑤
				① ② ③ ④ ⑤
				① ② ③ ④ ⑤
				① ② ③ ④ ⑤

Intake
Calories _____
Carbs _____
Fat _____
Protein _____
Activity (minutes)
Aerobic _____
Strengthening _____
Other _____

DATE _____

Time	Food(s)	Location	Emotional state	Hunger rating
				① ② ③ ④ ⑤
				① ② ③ ④ ⑤
				① ② ③ ④ ⑤
				① ② ③ ④ ⑤
				① ② ③ ④ ⑤
				① ② ③ ④ ⑤
				① ② ③ ④ ⑤

Intake
Calories _____
Carbs _____
Fat _____
Protein _____
Activity (minutes)
Aerobic _____
Strengthening _____
Other _____

DATE _____

Time	Food(s)	Location	Emotional state	Hunger rating
				① ② ③ ④ ⑤
				① ② ③ ④ ⑤
				① ② ③ ④ ⑤
				① ② ③ ④ ⑤
				① ② ③ ④ ⑤
				① ② ③ ④ ⑤
				① ② ③ ④ ⑤

Intake
Calories _____
Carbs _____
Fat _____
Protein _____
Activity (minutes)
Aerobic _____
Strengthening _____
Other _____

DATE _____

Time	Food(s)	Location	Emotional state	Hunger rating
				① ② ③ ④ ⑤
				① ② ③ ④ ⑤
				① ② ③ ④ ⑤
				① ② ③ ④ ⑤
				① ② ③ ④ ⑤
				① ② ③ ④ ⑤
				① ② ③ ④ ⑤

Intake
Calories _____
Carbs _____
Fat _____
Protein _____
Activity (minutes)
Aerobic _____
Strengthening _____
Other _____

MONTH _____ YEAR _____

Intake
Calories _____
Carbs _____
Fat _____
Protein _____

Activity (minutes)
Aerobic _____
Strengthening _____
Other _____

DATE _____

Time	Food(s)	Location	Emotional state	Hunger rating
				① ② ③ ④ ⑤
				① ② ③ ④ ⑤
				① ② ③ ④ ⑤
				① ② ③ ④ ⑤
				① ② ③ ④ ⑤
				① ② ③ ④ ⑤
				① ② ③ ④ ⑤

Intake
Calories _____
Carbs _____
Fat _____
Protein _____

Activity (minutes)
Aerobic _____
Strengthening _____
Other _____

DATE _____

Time	Food(s)	Location	Emotional state	Hunger rating
				① ② ③ ④ ⑤
				① ② ③ ④ ⑤
				① ② ③ ④ ⑤
				① ② ③ ④ ⑤
				① ② ③ ④ ⑤
				① ② ③ ④ ⑤
				① ② ③ ④ ⑤

Intake
Calories _____
Carbs _____
Fat _____
Protein _____

Activity (minutes)
Aerobic _____
Strengthening _____
Other _____

DATE _____

Time	Food(s)	Location	Emotional state	Hunger rating
				① ② ③ ④ ⑤
				① ② ③ ④ ⑤
				① ② ③ ④ ⑤
				① ② ③ ④ ⑤
				① ② ③ ④ ⑤
				① ② ③ ④ ⑤
				① ② ③ ④ ⑤

HOW AM I DOING?

MEASUREMENTS			WEIGHT		NOTES
	At diet's start	This month	Beginning weight	_____ pounds	_____
Chest	_____ inches	_____ inches	This month's weight	_____ pounds	_____
Upper arms	_____ inches	_____ inches	Total lost so far	_____ pounds	_____
Waist	_____ inches	_____ inches			_____
Hips	_____ inches	_____ inches			_____
Thighs	_____ inches	_____ inches			_____

WEEK _____

DATE _____

Time	Food(s)	Location	Emotional state	Hunger rating
				① ② ③ ④ ⑤
				① ② ③ ④ ⑤
				① ② ③ ④ ⑤
				① ② ③ ④ ⑤
				① ② ③ ④ ⑤
				① ② ③ ④ ⑤
				① ② ③ ④ ⑤

Intake
Calories _____
Carbs _____
Fat _____
Protein _____

Activity (minutes)
Aerobic _____
Strengthening _____
Other _____

DATE _____

Time	Food(s)	Location	Emotional state	Hunger rating
				① ② ③ ④ ⑤
				① ② ③ ④ ⑤
				① ② ③ ④ ⑤
				① ② ③ ④ ⑤
				① ② ③ ④ ⑤
				① ② ③ ④ ⑤
				① ② ③ ④ ⑤

Intake
Calories _____
Carbs _____
Fat _____
Protein _____

Activity (minutes)
Aerobic _____
Strengthening _____
Other _____

DATE _____

Time	Food(s)	Location	Emotional state	Hunger rating
				① ② ③ ④ ⑤
				① ② ③ ④ ⑤
				① ② ③ ④ ⑤
				① ② ③ ④ ⑤
				① ② ③ ④ ⑤
				① ② ③ ④ ⑤
				① ② ③ ④ ⑤

Intake
Calories _____
Carbs _____
Fat _____
Protein _____

Activity (minutes)
Aerobic _____
Strengthening _____
Other _____

DATE _____

Time	Food(s)	Location	Emotional state	Hunger rating
				① ② ③ ④ ⑤
				① ② ③ ④ ⑤
				① ② ③ ④ ⑤
				① ② ③ ④ ⑤
				① ② ③ ④ ⑤
				① ② ③ ④ ⑤
				① ② ③ ④ ⑤

Intake
Calories _____
Carbs _____
Fat _____
Protein _____

Activity (minutes)
Aerobic _____
Strengthening _____
Other _____

Intake

Calories _____

Carbs _____

Fat _____

Protein _____

Activity (minutes)

Aerobic _____

Strengthening _____

Other _____

DATE _____

Time	Food(s)	Location	Emotional state	Hunger rating
				① ② ③ ④ ⑤
				① ② ③ ④ ⑤
				① ② ③ ④ ⑤
				① ② ③ ④ ⑤
				① ② ③ ④ ⑤
				① ② ③ ④ ⑤
				① ② ③ ④ ⑤

Intake

Calories _____

Carbs _____

Fat _____

Protein _____

Activity (minutes)

Aerobic _____

Strengthening _____

Other _____

DATE _____

Time	Food(s)	Location	Emotional state	Hunger rating
				① ② ③ ④ ⑤
				① ② ③ ④ ⑤
				① ② ③ ④ ⑤
				① ② ③ ④ ⑤
				① ② ③ ④ ⑤
				① ② ③ ④ ⑤
				① ② ③ ④ ⑤

Intake

Calories _____

Carbs _____

Fat _____

Protein _____

Activity (minutes)

Aerobic _____

Strengthening _____

Other _____

DATE _____

Time	Food(s)	Location	Emotional state	Hunger rating
				① ② ③ ④ ⑤
				① ② ③ ④ ⑤
				① ② ③ ④ ⑤
				① ② ③ ④ ⑤
				① ② ③ ④ ⑤
				① ② ③ ④ ⑤
				① ② ③ ④ ⑤

HOW AM I DOING?

Weekly Weight Check

_____ pounds

_____ total lost

TIP FOR THE WEEK

If you keep taking steps that move you forward, you will always be heading in the right direction.

☐ DONE!

WEEK _____

DATE _____

Time	Food(s)	Location	Emotional state	Hunger rating
				① ② ③ ④ ⑤
				① ② ③ ④ ⑤
				① ② ③ ④ ⑤
				① ② ③ ④ ⑤
				① ② ③ ④ ⑤
				① ② ③ ④ ⑤
				① ② ③ ④ ⑤

Intake
Calories _____
Carbs _____
Fat _____
Protein _____
Activity (minutes)
Aerobic _____
Strengthening _____
Other _____

DATE _____

Time	Food(s)	Location	Emotional state	Hunger rating
				① ② ③ ④ ⑤
				① ② ③ ④ ⑤
				① ② ③ ④ ⑤
				① ② ③ ④ ⑤
				① ② ③ ④ ⑤
				① ② ③ ④ ⑤
				① ② ③ ④ ⑤

Intake
Calories _____
Carbs _____
Fat _____
Protein _____
Activity (minutes)
Aerobic _____
Strengthening _____
Other _____

DATE _____

Time	Food(s)	Location	Emotional state	Hunger rating
				① ② ③ ④ ⑤
				① ② ③ ④ ⑤
				① ② ③ ④ ⑤
				① ② ③ ④ ⑤
				① ② ③ ④ ⑤
				① ② ③ ④ ⑤
				① ② ③ ④ ⑤

Intake
Calories _____
Carbs _____
Fat _____
Protein _____
Activity (minutes)
Aerobic _____
Strengthening _____
Other _____

DATE _____

Time	Food(s)	Location	Emotional state	Hunger rating
				① ② ③ ④ ⑤
				① ② ③ ④ ⑤
				① ② ③ ④ ⑤
				① ② ③ ④ ⑤
				① ② ③ ④ ⑤
				① ② ③ ④ ⑤
				① ② ③ ④ ⑤

Intake
Calories _____
Carbs _____
Fat _____
Protein _____
Activity (minutes)
Aerobic _____
Strengthening _____
Other _____

MONTH _____ YEAR _____

Intake
Calories _____
Carbs _____
Fat _____
Protein _____

Activity (minutes)
Aerobic _____
Strengthening _____
Other _____

DATE _____

Time	Food(s)	Location	Emotional state	Hunger rating
				① ② ③ ④ ⑤
				① ② ③ ④ ⑤
				① ② ③ ④ ⑤
				① ② ③ ④ ⑤
				① ② ③ ④ ⑤
				① ② ③ ④ ⑤
				① ② ③ ④ ⑤

Intake
Calories _____
Carbs _____
Fat _____
Protein _____

Activity (minutes)
Aerobic _____
Strengthening _____
Other _____

DATE _____

Time	Food(s)	Location	Emotional state	Hunger rating
				① ② ③ ④ ⑤
				① ② ③ ④ ⑤
				① ② ③ ④ ⑤
				① ② ③ ④ ⑤
				① ② ③ ④ ⑤
				① ② ③ ④ ⑤
				① ② ③ ④ ⑤

Intake
Calories _____
Carbs _____
Fat _____
Protein _____

Activity (minutes)
Aerobic _____
Strengthening _____
Other _____

DATE _____

Time	Food(s)	Location	Emotional state	Hunger rating
				① ② ③ ④ ⑤
				① ② ③ ④ ⑤
				① ② ③ ④ ⑤
				① ② ③ ④ ⑤
				① ② ③ ④ ⑤
				① ② ③ ④ ⑤
				① ② ③ ④ ⑤

HOW AM I DOING?

Weekly Weight Check

_____ pounds
_____ total lost

TIP FOR THE WEEK

If you don't have a lot of weight left to lose but it's not coming off fast, don't be discouraged. The less weight you have to lose, the slower your weight loss is likely to be.

☐ DONE!

WEEK _____

DATE _____

Time	Food(s)	Location	Emotional state	Hunger rating
				① ② ③ ④ ⑤
				① ② ③ ④ ⑤
				① ② ③ ④ ⑤
				① ② ③ ④ ⑤
				① ② ③ ④ ⑤
				① ② ③ ④ ⑤
				① ② ③ ④ ⑤

Intake
Calories _____
Carbs _____
Fat _____
Protein _____

Activity (minutes)
Aerobic _____
Strengthening _____
Other _____

DATE _____

Time	Food(s)	Location	Emotional state	Hunger rating
				① ② ③ ④ ⑤
				① ② ③ ④ ⑤
				① ② ③ ④ ⑤
				① ② ③ ④ ⑤
				① ② ③ ④ ⑤
				① ② ③ ④ ⑤
				① ② ③ ④ ⑤

Intake
Calories _____
Carbs _____
Fat _____
Protein _____

Activity (minutes)
Aerobic _____
Strengthening _____
Other _____

DATE _____

Time	Food(s)	Location	Emotional state	Hunger rating
				① ② ③ ④ ⑤
				① ② ③ ④ ⑤
				① ② ③ ④ ⑤
				① ② ③ ④ ⑤
				① ② ③ ④ ⑤
				① ② ③ ④ ⑤
				① ② ③ ④ ⑤

Intake
Calories _____
Carbs _____
Fat _____
Protein _____

Activity (minutes)
Aerobic _____
Strengthening _____
Other _____

DATE _____

Time	Food(s)	Location	Emotional state	Hunger rating
				① ② ③ ④ ⑤
				① ② ③ ④ ⑤
				① ② ③ ④ ⑤
				① ② ③ ④ ⑤
				① ② ③ ④ ⑤
				① ② ③ ④ ⑤
				① ② ③ ④ ⑤

Intake
Calories _____
Carbs _____
Fat _____
Protein _____

Activity (minutes)
Aerobic _____
Strengthening _____
Other _____

MONTH _____ YEAR _____

Intake
Calories _____
Carbs _____
Fat _____
Protein _____
Activity (minutes)
Aerobic _____
Strengthening _____
Other _____

DATE _____

Time	Food(s)	Location	Emotional state	Hunger rating
				① ② ③ ④ ⑤
				① ② ③ ④ ⑤
				① ② ③ ④ ⑤
				① ② ③ ④ ⑤
				① ② ③ ④ ⑤
				① ② ③ ④ ⑤
				① ② ③ ④ ⑤

Intake
Calories _____
Carbs _____
Fat _____
Protein _____
Activity (minutes)
Aerobic _____
Strengthening _____
Other _____

DATE _____

Time	Food(s)	Location	Emotional state	Hunger rating
				① ② ③ ④ ⑤
				① ② ③ ④ ⑤
				① ② ③ ④ ⑤
				① ② ③ ④ ⑤
				① ② ③ ④ ⑤
				① ② ③ ④ ⑤
				① ② ③ ④ ⑤

Intake
Calories _____
Carbs _____
Fat _____
Protein _____
Activity (minutes)
Aerobic _____
Strengthening _____
Other _____

DATE _____

Time	Food(s)	Location	Emotional state	Hunger rating
				① ② ③ ④ ⑤
				① ② ③ ④ ⑤
				① ② ③ ④ ⑤
				① ② ③ ④ ⑤
				① ② ③ ④ ⑤
				① ② ③ ④ ⑤
				① ② ③ ④ ⑤

How Am I Doing?

Weekly Weight Check

_____ pounds
_____ total lost

TIP FOR THE WEEK

Go brush your teeth! If you're craving a snack, especially carb-laden foods, brush your teeth. The taste of the minty toothpaste will squelch your craving. Keep a travel-size toothbrush and toothpaste in your purse or in a desk drawer at work for a craving emergency.

❒ DONE!

Week _____

Date _____

Time	Food(s)	Location	Emotional state	Hunger rating
				① ② ③ ④ ⑤
				① ② ③ ④ ⑤
				① ② ③ ④ ⑤
				① ② ③ ④ ⑤
				① ② ③ ④ ⑤
				① ② ③ ④ ⑤
				① ② ③ ④ ⑤

Intake
Calories _____
Carbs _____
Fat _____
Protein _____
Activity (minutes)
Aerobic _____
Strengthening _____
Other _____

Date _____

Time	Food(s)	Location	Emotional state	Hunger rating
				① ② ③ ④ ⑤
				① ② ③ ④ ⑤
				① ② ③ ④ ⑤
				① ② ③ ④ ⑤
				① ② ③ ④ ⑤
				① ② ③ ④ ⑤
				① ② ③ ④ ⑤

Intake
Calories _____
Carbs _____
Fat _____
Protein _____
Activity (minutes)
Aerobic _____
Strengthening _____
Other _____

Date _____

Time	Food(s)	Location	Emotional state	Hunger rating
				① ② ③ ④ ⑤
				① ② ③ ④ ⑤
				① ② ③ ④ ⑤
				① ② ③ ④ ⑤
				① ② ③ ④ ⑤
				① ② ③ ④ ⑤
				① ② ③ ④ ⑤

Intake
Calories _____
Carbs _____
Fat _____
Protein _____
Activity (minutes)
Aerobic _____
Strengthening _____
Other _____

Date _____

Time	Food(s)	Location	Emotional state	Hunger rating
				① ② ③ ④ ⑤
				① ② ③ ④ ⑤
				① ② ③ ④ ⑤
				① ② ③ ④ ⑤
				① ② ③ ④ ⑤
				① ② ③ ④ ⑤
				① ② ③ ④ ⑤

Intake
Calories _____
Carbs _____
Fat _____
Protein _____
Activity (minutes)
Aerobic _____
Strengthening _____
Other _____

MONTH _____ YEAR _____

Intake
Calories _____
Carbs _____
Fat _____
Protein _____

Activity (minutes)
Aerobic _____
Strengthening _____
Other _____

DATE _____

Time	Food(s)	Location	Emotional state	Hunger rating
				① ② ③ ④ ⑤
				① ② ③ ④ ⑤
				① ② ③ ④ ⑤
				① ② ③ ④ ⑤
				① ② ③ ④ ⑤
				① ② ③ ④ ⑤
				① ② ③ ④ ⑤

Intake
Calories _____
Carbs _____
Fat _____
Protein _____

Activity (minutes)
Aerobic _____
Strengthening _____
Other _____

DATE _____

Time	Food(s)	Location	Emotional state	Hunger rating
				① ② ③ ④ ⑤
				① ② ③ ④ ⑤
				① ② ③ ④ ⑤
				① ② ③ ④ ⑤
				① ② ③ ④ ⑤
				① ② ③ ④ ⑤
				① ② ③ ④ ⑤

Intake
Calories _____
Carbs _____
Fat _____
Protein _____

Activity (minutes)
Aerobic _____
Strengthening _____
Other _____

DATE _____

Time	Food(s)	Location	Emotional state	Hunger rating
				① ② ③ ④ ⑤
				① ② ③ ④ ⑤
				① ② ③ ④ ⑤
				① ② ③ ④ ⑤
				① ② ③ ④ ⑤
				① ② ③ ④ ⑤
				① ② ③ ④ ⑤

HOW AM I DOING?

MEASUREMENTS	At diet's start	This month	WEIGHT		NOTES
Chest	_____ inches	_____ inches	Beginning weight	_____ pounds	_____
Upper arms	_____ inches	_____ inches	This month's weight	_____ pounds	_____
Waist	_____ inches	_____ inches	Total lost so far	_____ pounds	_____
Hips	_____ inches	_____ inches			_____
Thighs	_____ inches	_____ inches			_____

WEEK _____

DATE _____

Time	Food(s)	Location	Emotional state	Hunger rating
				① ② ③ ④ ⑤
				① ② ③ ④ ⑤
				① ② ③ ④ ⑤
				① ② ③ ④ ⑤
				① ② ③ ④ ⑤
				① ② ③ ④ ⑤
				① ② ③ ④ ⑤

Intake
Calories _____
Carbs _____
Fat _____
Protein _____
Activity (minutes)
Aerobic _____
Strengthening _____
Other _____

DATE _____

Time	Food(s)	Location	Emotional state	Hunger rating
				① ② ③ ④ ⑤
				① ② ③ ④ ⑤
				① ② ③ ④ ⑤
				① ② ③ ④ ⑤
				① ② ③ ④ ⑤
				① ② ③ ④ ⑤
				① ② ③ ④ ⑤

Intake
Calories _____
Carbs _____
Fat _____
Protein _____
Activity (minutes)
Aerobic _____
Strengthening _____
Other _____

DATE _____

Time	Food(s)	Location	Emotional state	Hunger rating
				① ② ③ ④ ⑤
				① ② ③ ④ ⑤
				① ② ③ ④ ⑤
				① ② ③ ④ ⑤
				① ② ③ ④ ⑤
				① ② ③ ④ ⑤
				① ② ③ ④ ⑤

Intake
Calories _____
Carbs _____
Fat _____
Protein _____
Activity (minutes)
Aerobic _____
Strengthening _____
Other _____

DATE _____

Time	Food(s)	Location	Emotional state	Hunger rating
				① ② ③ ④ ⑤
				① ② ③ ④ ⑤
				① ② ③ ④ ⑤
				① ② ③ ④ ⑤
				① ② ③ ④ ⑤
				① ② ③ ④ ⑤
				① ② ③ ④ ⑤

Intake
Calories _____
Carbs _____
Fat _____
Protein _____
Activity (minutes)
Aerobic _____
Strengthening _____
Other _____

MONTH _____ YEAR _____

Intake
Calories _____
Carbs _____
Fat _____
Protein _____

Activity (minutes)
Aerobic _____
Strengthening _____
Other _____

DATE _____

Time	Food(s)	Location	Emotional state	Hunger rating
				① ② ③ ④ ⑤
				① ② ③ ④ ⑤
				① ② ③ ④ ⑤
				① ② ③ ④ ⑤
				① ② ③ ④ ⑤
				① ② ③ ④ ⑤
				① ② ③ ④ ⑤

Intake
Calories _____
Carbs _____
Fat _____
Protein _____

Activity (minutes)
Aerobic _____
Strengthening _____
Other _____

DATE _____

Time	Food(s)	Location	Emotional state	Hunger rating
				① ② ③ ④ ⑤
				① ② ③ ④ ⑤
				① ② ③ ④ ⑤
				① ② ③ ④ ⑤
				① ② ③ ④ ⑤
				① ② ③ ④ ⑤
				① ② ③ ④ ⑤

Intake
Calories _____
Carbs _____
Fat _____
Protein _____

Activity (minutes)
Aerobic _____
Strengthening _____
Other _____

DATE _____

Time	Food(s)	Location	Emotional state	Hunger rating
				① ② ③ ④ ⑤
				① ② ③ ④ ⑤
				① ② ③ ④ ⑤
				① ② ③ ④ ⑤
				① ② ③ ④ ⑤
				① ② ③ ④ ⑤
				① ② ③ ④ ⑤

HOW AM I DOING?

Weekly Weight Check

_____ pounds
_____ total lost

TIP FOR THE WEEK

Sometimes we confuse hunger with thirst. When you think you're hungry, try drinking a glass of water. It may be what your body really wanted.

❒ DONE!

DATE _____

Time	Food(s)	Location	Emotional state	Hunger rating
				① ② ③ ④ ⑤
				① ② ③ ④ ⑤
				① ② ③ ④ ⑤
				① ② ③ ④ ⑤
				① ② ③ ④ ⑤
				① ② ③ ④ ⑤
				① ② ③ ④ ⑤

Intake

Calories _____
Carbs _____
Fat _____
Protein _____

Activity (minutes)

Aerobic _____
Strengthening _____
Other _____

DATE _____

Time	Food(s)	Location	Emotional state	Hunger rating
				① ② ③ ④ ⑤
				① ② ③ ④ ⑤
				① ② ③ ④ ⑤
				① ② ③ ④ ⑤
				① ② ③ ④ ⑤
				① ② ③ ④ ⑤
				① ② ③ ④ ⑤

Intake

Calories _____
Carbs _____
Fat _____
Protein _____

Activity (minutes)

Aerobic _____
Strengthening _____
Other _____

DATE _____

Time	Food(s)	Location	Emotional state	Hunger rating
				① ② ③ ④ ⑤
				① ② ③ ④ ⑤
				① ② ③ ④ ⑤
				① ② ③ ④ ⑤
				① ② ③ ④ ⑤
				① ② ③ ④ ⑤
				① ② ③ ④ ⑤

Intake

Calories _____
Carbs _____
Fat _____
Protein _____

Activity (minutes)

Aerobic _____
Strengthening _____
Other _____

DATE _____

Time	Food(s)	Location	Emotional state	Hunger rating
				① ② ③ ④ ⑤
				① ② ③ ④ ⑤
				① ② ③ ④ ⑤
				① ② ③ ④ ⑤
				① ② ③ ④ ⑤
				① ② ③ ④ ⑤
				① ② ③ ④ ⑤

Intake

Calories _____
Carbs _____
Fat _____
Protein _____

Activity (minutes)

Aerobic _____
Strengthening _____
Other _____

Intake

Calories _____
Carbs _____
Fat _____
Protein _____

Activity (minutes)

Aerobic _____
Strengthening _____
Other _____

DATE _____

Time	Food(s)	Location	Emotional state	Hunger rating
				① ② ③ ④ ⑤
				① ② ③ ④ ⑤
				① ② ③ ④ ⑤
				① ② ③ ④ ⑤
				① ② ③ ④ ⑤
				① ② ③ ④ ⑤
				① ② ③ ④ ⑤

Intake

Calories _____
Carbs _____
Fat _____
Protein _____

Activity (minutes)

Aerobic _____
Strengthening _____
Other _____

DATE _____

Time	Food(s)	Location	Emotional state	Hunger rating
				① ② ③ ④ ⑤
				① ② ③ ④ ⑤
				① ② ③ ④ ⑤
				① ② ③ ④ ⑤
				① ② ③ ④ ⑤
				① ② ③ ④ ⑤
				① ② ③ ④ ⑤

Intake

Calories _____
Carbs _____
Fat _____
Protein _____

Activity (minutes)

Aerobic _____
Strengthening _____
Other _____

DATE _____

Time	Food(s)	Location	Emotional state	Hunger rating
				① ② ③ ④ ⑤
				① ② ③ ④ ⑤
				① ② ③ ④ ⑤
				① ② ③ ④ ⑤
				① ② ③ ④ ⑤
				① ② ③ ④ ⑤
				① ② ③ ④ ⑤

HOW AM I DOING?

Weekly Weight Check

_____ pounds
_____ total lost

TIP FOR THE WEEK

Chew on it! The more you chew your food, the more satisfied you will feel. And if you're hungry, try chewing on a piece of sugarless gum. Sometimes chewing, not eating, is all you need.

☐ DONE!

WEEK _____

DATE _____

Time	Food(s)	Location	Emotional state	Hunger rating
				① ② ③ ④ ⑤
				① ② ③ ④ ⑤
				① ② ③ ④ ⑤
				① ② ③ ④ ⑤
				① ② ③ ④ ⑤
				① ② ③ ④ ⑤
				① ② ③ ④ ⑤

Intake

Calories _____
Carbs _____
Fat _____
Protein _____

Activity (minutes)

Aerobic _____
Strengthening _____
Other _____

DATE _____

Time	Food(s)	Location	Emotional state	Hunger rating
				① ② ③ ④ ⑤
				① ② ③ ④ ⑤
				① ② ③ ④ ⑤
				① ② ③ ④ ⑤
				① ② ③ ④ ⑤
				① ② ③ ④ ⑤
				① ② ③ ④ ⑤

Intake

Calories _____
Carbs _____
Fat _____
Protein _____

Activity (minutes)

Aerobic _____
Strengthening _____
Other _____

DATE _____

Time	Food(s)	Location	Emotional state	Hunger rating
				① ② ③ ④ ⑤
				① ② ③ ④ ⑤
				① ② ③ ④ ⑤
				① ② ③ ④ ⑤
				① ② ③ ④ ⑤
				① ② ③ ④ ⑤
				① ② ③ ④ ⑤

Intake

Calories _____
Carbs _____
Fat _____
Protein _____

Activity (minutes)

Aerobic _____
Strengthening _____
Other _____

DATE _____

Time	Food(s)	Location	Emotional state	Hunger rating
				① ② ③ ④ ⑤
				① ② ③ ④ ⑤
				① ② ③ ④ ⑤
				① ② ③ ④ ⑤
				① ② ③ ④ ⑤
				① ② ③ ④ ⑤
				① ② ③ ④ ⑤

Intake

Calories _____
Carbs _____
Fat _____
Protein _____

Activity (minutes)

Aerobic _____
Strengthening _____
Other _____

MONTH _____ YEAR _____

Intake
Calories _____
Carbs _____
Fat _____
Protein _____

Activity (minutes)
Aerobic _____
Strengthening _____
Other _____

DATE _____

Time	Food(s)	Location	Emotional state	Hunger rating
				① ② ③ ④ ⑤
				① ② ③ ④ ⑤
				① ② ③ ④ ⑤
				① ② ③ ④ ⑤
				① ② ③ ④ ⑤
				① ② ③ ④ ⑤
				① ② ③ ④ ⑤

Intake
Calories _____
Carbs _____
Fat _____
Protein _____

Activity (minutes)
Aerobic _____
Strengthening _____
Other _____

DATE _____

Time	Food(s)	Location	Emotional state	Hunger rating
				① ② ③ ④ ⑤
				① ② ③ ④ ⑤
				① ② ③ ④ ⑤
				① ② ③ ④ ⑤
				① ② ③ ④ ⑤
				① ② ③ ④ ⑤
				① ② ③ ④ ⑤

Intake
Calories _____
Carbs _____
Fat _____
Protein _____

Activity (minutes)
Aerobic _____
Strengthening _____
Other _____

DATE _____

Time	Food(s)	Location	Emotional state	Hunger rating
				① ② ③ ④ ⑤
				① ② ③ ④ ⑤
				① ② ③ ④ ⑤
				① ② ③ ④ ⑤
				① ② ③ ④ ⑤
				① ② ③ ④ ⑤
				① ② ③ ④ ⑤

HOW AM I DOING?

Weekly Weight Check

_____ pounds
_____ total lost

TIP FOR THE WEEK

Don't measure your progress by the scale alone. Muscle weighs more than fat. If you're exercising, you've surely lost body fat even if the number on the scale hasn't dropped much or at all. Muscle takes up less space than fat, so you will appear slimmer and your clothes will be looser.

❑ **DONE!**

WEEK _____

DATE _____

Time	Food(s)	Location	Emotional state	Hunger rating
				① ② ③ ④ ⑤
				① ② ③ ④ ⑤
				① ② ③ ④ ⑤
				① ② ③ ④ ⑤
				① ② ③ ④ ⑤
				① ② ③ ④ ⑤
				① ② ③ ④ ⑤

Intake
Calories _____
Carbs _____
Fat _____
Protein _____
Activity (minutes)
Aerobic _____
Strengthening _____
Other _____

DATE _____

Time	Food(s)	Location	Emotional state	Hunger rating
				① ② ③ ④ ⑤
				① ② ③ ④ ⑤
				① ② ③ ④ ⑤
				① ② ③ ④ ⑤
				① ② ③ ④ ⑤
				① ② ③ ④ ⑤
				① ② ③ ④ ⑤

Intake
Calories _____
Carbs _____
Fat _____
Protein _____
Activity (minutes)
Aerobic _____
Strengthening _____
Other _____

DATE _____

Time	Food(s)	Location	Emotional state	Hunger rating
				① ② ③ ④ ⑤
				① ② ③ ④ ⑤
				① ② ③ ④ ⑤
				① ② ③ ④ ⑤
				① ② ③ ④ ⑤
				① ② ③ ④ ⑤
				① ② ③ ④ ⑤

Intake
Calories _____
Carbs _____
Fat _____
Protein _____
Activity (minutes)
Aerobic _____
Strengthening _____
Other _____

DATE _____

Time	Food(s)	Location	Emotional state	Hunger rating
				① ② ③ ④ ⑤
				① ② ③ ④ ⑤
				① ② ③ ④ ⑤
				① ② ③ ④ ⑤
				① ② ③ ④ ⑤
				① ② ③ ④ ⑤
				① ② ③ ④ ⑤

Intake
Calories _____
Carbs _____
Fat _____
Protein _____
Activity (minutes)
Aerobic _____
Strengthening _____
Other _____

MONTH _____ YEAR _____

Intake
Calories _____
Carbs _____
Fat _____
Protein _____

Activity (minutes)
Aerobic _____
Strengthening _____
Other _____

DATE _____

Time	Food(s)	Location	Emotional state	Hunger rating
				① ② ③ ④ ⑤
				① ② ③ ④ ⑤
				① ② ③ ④ ⑤
				① ② ③ ④ ⑤
				① ② ③ ④ ⑤
				① ② ③ ④ ⑤
				① ② ③ ④ ⑤

Intake
Calories _____
Carbs _____
Fat _____
Protein _____

Activity (minutes)
Aerobic _____
Strengthening _____
Other _____

DATE _____

Time	Food(s)	Location	Emotional state	Hunger rating
				① ② ③ ④ ⑤
				① ② ③ ④ ⑤
				① ② ③ ④ ⑤
				① ② ③ ④ ⑤
				① ② ③ ④ ⑤
				① ② ③ ④ ⑤
				① ② ③ ④ ⑤

Intake
Calories _____
Carbs _____
Fat _____
Protein _____

Activity (minutes)
Aerobic _____
Strengthening _____
Other _____

DATE _____

Time	Food(s)	Location	Emotional state	Hunger rating
				① ② ③ ④ ⑤
				① ② ③ ④ ⑤
				① ② ③ ④ ⑤
				① ② ③ ④ ⑤
				① ② ③ ④ ⑤
				① ② ③ ④ ⑤
				① ② ③ ④ ⑤

HOW AM I DOING?

MEASUREMENTS			WEIGHT		NOTES
	At diet's start	This month			
Chest	_____ inches	_____ inches	Beginning weight _____ pounds		_____
Upper arms	_____ inches	_____ inches	This month's weight _____ pounds		_____
Waist	_____ inches	_____ inches	Total lost so far _____ pounds		_____
Hips	_____ inches	_____ inches			_____
Thighs	_____ inches	_____ inches			_____
					_____

WEEK _____

DATE _____

Time	Food(s)	Location	Emotional state	Hunger rating
				① ② ③ ④ ⑤
				① ② ③ ④ ⑤
				① ② ③ ④ ⑤
				① ② ③ ④ ⑤
				① ② ③ ④ ⑤
				① ② ③ ④ ⑤
				① ② ③ ④ ⑤

Intake
Calories _____
Carbs _____
Fat _____
Protein _____

Activity (minutes)
Aerobic _____
Strengthening _____
Other _____

DATE _____

Time	Food(s)	Location	Emotional state	Hunger rating
				① ② ③ ④ ⑤
				① ② ③ ④ ⑤
				① ② ③ ④ ⑤
				① ② ③ ④ ⑤
				① ② ③ ④ ⑤
				① ② ③ ④ ⑤
				① ② ③ ④ ⑤

Intake
Calories _____
Carbs _____
Fat _____
Protein _____

Activity (minutes)
Aerobic _____
Strengthening _____
Other _____

DATE _____

Time	Food(s)	Location	Emotional state	Hunger rating
				① ② ③ ④ ⑤
				① ② ③ ④ ⑤
				① ② ③ ④ ⑤
				① ② ③ ④ ⑤
				① ② ③ ④ ⑤
				① ② ③ ④ ⑤
				① ② ③ ④ ⑤

Intake
Calories _____
Carbs _____
Fat _____
Protein _____

Activity (minutes)
Aerobic _____
Strengthening _____
Other _____

DATE _____

Time	Food(s)	Location	Emotional state	Hunger rating
				① ② ③ ④ ⑤
				① ② ③ ④ ⑤
				① ② ③ ④ ⑤
				① ② ③ ④ ⑤
				① ② ③ ④ ⑤
				① ② ③ ④ ⑤
				① ② ③ ④ ⑤

Intake
Calories _____
Carbs _____
Fat _____
Protein _____

Activity (minutes)
Aerobic _____
Strengthening _____
Other _____

Intake

Calories _____
Carbs _____
Fat _____
Protein _____

Activity (minutes)

Aerobic _____
Strengthening _____
Other _____

DATE _____

Time	Food(s)	Location	Emotional state	Hunger rating
				① ② ③ ④ ⑤
				① ② ③ ④ ⑤
				① ② ③ ④ ⑤
				① ② ③ ④ ⑤
				① ② ③ ④ ⑤
				① ② ③ ④ ⑤
				① ② ③ ④ ⑤

Intake

Calories _____
Carbs _____
Fat _____
Protein _____

Activity (minutes)

Aerobic _____
Strengthening _____
Other _____

DATE _____

Time	Food(s)	Location	Emotional state	Hunger rating
				① ② ③ ④ ⑤
				① ② ③ ④ ⑤
				① ② ③ ④ ⑤
				① ② ③ ④ ⑤
				① ② ③ ④ ⑤
				① ② ③ ④ ⑤
				① ② ③ ④ ⑤

Intake

Calories _____
Carbs _____
Fat _____
Protein _____

Activity (minutes)

Aerobic _____
Strengthening _____
Other _____

DATE _____

Time	Food(s)	Location	Emotional state	Hunger rating
				① ② ③ ④ ⑤
				① ② ③ ④ ⑤
				① ② ③ ④ ⑤
				① ② ③ ④ ⑤
				① ② ③ ④ ⑤
				① ② ③ ④ ⑤
				① ② ③ ④ ⑤

HOW AM I DOING?

Weekly Weight Check

_____ pounds
_____ total lost

TIP FOR THE WEEK

Perseverance is the key to success.

☐ DONE!

WEEK _____

DATE _____

Time	Food(s)	Location	Emotional state	Hunger rating
				① ② ③ ④ ⑤
				① ② ③ ④ ⑤
				① ② ③ ④ ⑤
				① ② ③ ④ ⑤
				① ② ③ ④ ⑤
				① ② ③ ④ ⑤
				① ② ③ ④ ⑤

Intake
Calories _____
Carbs _____
Fat _____
Protein _____
Activity (minutes)
Aerobic _____
Strengthening _____
Other _____

DATE _____

Time	Food(s)	Location	Emotional state	Hunger rating
				① ② ③ ④ ⑤
				① ② ③ ④ ⑤
				① ② ③ ④ ⑤
				① ② ③ ④ ⑤
				① ② ③ ④ ⑤
				① ② ③ ④ ⑤
				① ② ③ ④ ⑤

Intake
Calories _____
Carbs _____
Fat _____
Protein _____
Activity (minutes)
Aerobic _____
Strengthening _____
Other _____

DATE _____

Time	Food(s)	Location	Emotional state	Hunger rating
				① ② ③ ④ ⑤
				① ② ③ ④ ⑤
				① ② ③ ④ ⑤
				① ② ③ ④ ⑤
				① ② ③ ④ ⑤
				① ② ③ ④ ⑤
				① ② ③ ④ ⑤

Intake
Calories _____
Carbs _____
Fat _____
Protein _____
Activity (minutes)
Aerobic _____
Strengthening _____
Other _____

DATE _____

Time	Food(s)	Location	Emotional state	Hunger rating
				① ② ③ ④ ⑤
				① ② ③ ④ ⑤
				① ② ③ ④ ⑤
				① ② ③ ④ ⑤
				① ② ③ ④ ⑤
				① ② ③ ④ ⑤
				① ② ③ ④ ⑤

Intake
Calories _____
Carbs _____
Fat _____
Protein _____
Activity (minutes)
Aerobic _____
Strengthening _____
Other _____

MONTH _____ YEAR _____

Intake

Calories _____

Carbs _____

Fat _____

Protein _____

Activity (minutes)

Aerobic _____

Strengthening _____

Other _____

DATE _____

Time	Food(s)	Location	Emotional state	Hunger rating
				① ② ③ ④ ⑤
				① ② ③ ④ ⑤
				① ② ③ ④ ⑤
				① ② ③ ④ ⑤
				① ② ③ ④ ⑤
				① ② ③ ④ ⑤
				① ② ③ ④ ⑤

Intake

Calories _____

Carbs _____

Fat _____

Protein _____

Activity (minutes)

Aerobic _____

Strengthening _____

Other _____

DATE _____

Time	Food(s)	Location	Emotional state	Hunger rating
				① ② ③ ④ ⑤
				① ② ③ ④ ⑤
				① ② ③ ④ ⑤
				① ② ③ ④ ⑤
				① ② ③ ④ ⑤
				① ② ③ ④ ⑤
				① ② ③ ④ ⑤

Intake

Calories _____

Carbs _____

Fat _____

Protein _____

Activity (minutes)

Aerobic _____

Strengthening _____

Other _____

DATE _____

Time	Food(s)	Location	Emotional state	Hunger rating
				① ② ③ ④ ⑤
				① ② ③ ④ ⑤
				① ② ③ ④ ⑤
				① ② ③ ④ ⑤
				① ② ③ ④ ⑤
				① ② ③ ④ ⑤
				① ② ③ ④ ⑤

HOW AM I DOING?

Weekly Weight Check

_____ pounds

_____ total lost

TIP FOR THE WEEK

Always choose a whole piece of fruit over fruit juice. Processed fruit juice has virtually no fiber and is loaded with fructose (sugar), which hits your bloodstream quickly. Whole fruit, on the other hand, has fiber, which slows the digestion of fructose and the release of sugar into your bloodstream.

☐ DONE!

WEEK _____

DATE _____

Time	Food(s)	Location	Emotional state	Hunger rating
				① ② ③ ④ ⑤
				① ② ③ ④ ⑤
				① ② ③ ④ ⑤
				① ② ③ ④ ⑤
				① ② ③ ④ ⑤
				① ② ③ ④ ⑤
				① ② ③ ④ ⑤

Intake
Calories _____
Carbs _____
Fat _____
Protein _____
Activity (minutes)
Aerobic _____
Strengthening _____
Other _____

DATE _____

Time	Food(s)	Location	Emotional state	Hunger rating
				① ② ③ ④ ⑤
				① ② ③ ④ ⑤
				① ② ③ ④ ⑤
				① ② ③ ④ ⑤
				① ② ③ ④ ⑤
				① ② ③ ④ ⑤
				① ② ③ ④ ⑤

Intake
Calories _____
Carbs _____
Fat _____
Protein _____
Activity (minutes)
Aerobic _____
Strengthening _____
Other _____

DATE _____

Time	Food(s)	Location	Emotional state	Hunger rating
				① ② ③ ④ ⑤
				① ② ③ ④ ⑤
				① ② ③ ④ ⑤
				① ② ③ ④ ⑤
				① ② ③ ④ ⑤
				① ② ③ ④ ⑤
				① ② ③ ④ ⑤

Intake
Calories _____
Carbs _____
Fat _____
Protein _____
Activity (minutes)
Aerobic _____
Strengthening _____
Other _____

DATE _____

Time	Food(s)	Location	Emotional state	Hunger rating
				① ② ③ ④ ⑤
				① ② ③ ④ ⑤
				① ② ③ ④ ⑤
				① ② ③ ④ ⑤
				① ② ③ ④ ⑤
				① ② ③ ④ ⑤
				① ② ③ ④ ⑤

Intake
Calories _____
Carbs _____
Fat _____
Protein _____
Activity (minutes)
Aerobic _____
Strengthening _____
Other _____

MONTH _____ YEAR _____

Intake
Calories _____
Carbs _____
Fat _____
Protein _____

Activity (minutes)
Aerobic _____
Strengthening _____
Other _____

DATE _____

Time	Food(s)	Location	Emotional state	Hunger rating
				① ② ③ ④ ⑤
				① ② ③ ④ ⑤
				① ② ③ ④ ⑤
				① ② ③ ④ ⑤
				① ② ③ ④ ⑤
				① ② ③ ④ ⑤
				① ② ③ ④ ⑤

Intake
Calories _____
Carbs _____
Fat _____
Protein _____

Activity (minutes)
Aerobic _____
Strengthening _____
Other _____

DATE _____

Time	Food(s)	Location	Emotional state	Hunger rating
				① ② ③ ④ ⑤
				① ② ③ ④ ⑤
				① ② ③ ④ ⑤
				① ② ③ ④ ⑤
				① ② ③ ④ ⑤
				① ② ③ ④ ⑤
				① ② ③ ④ ⑤

Intake
Calories _____
Carbs _____
Fat _____
Protein _____

Activity (minutes)
Aerobic _____
Strengthening _____
Other _____

DATE _____

Time	Food(s)	Location	Emotional state	Hunger rating
				① ② ③ ④ ⑤
				① ② ③ ④ ⑤
				① ② ③ ④ ⑤
				① ② ③ ④ ⑤
				① ② ③ ④ ⑤
				① ② ③ ④ ⑤
				① ② ③ ④ ⑤

HOW AM I DOING?

Weekly Weight Check

_____ pounds

_____ total lost

TIP FOR THE WEEK

Try eating four to six smaller meals every day. If you eat two small meals and then a large evening meal, you are likely to take in more calories.

☐ DONE!

DATE _____

Time	Food(s)	Location	Emotional state	Hunger rating
				① ② ③ ④ ⑤
				① ② ③ ④ ⑤
				① ② ③ ④ ⑤
				① ② ③ ④ ⑤
				① ② ③ ④ ⑤
				① ② ③ ④ ⑤
				① ② ③ ④ ⑤

Intake
Calories _____
Carbs _____
Fat _____
Protein _____
Activity (minutes)
Aerobic _____
Strengthening _____
Other _____

DATE _____

Time	Food(s)	Location	Emotional state	Hunger rating
				① ② ③ ④ ⑤
				① ② ③ ④ ⑤
				① ② ③ ④ ⑤
				① ② ③ ④ ⑤
				① ② ③ ④ ⑤
				① ② ③ ④ ⑤
				① ② ③ ④ ⑤

Intake
Calories _____
Carbs _____
Fat _____
Protein _____
Activity (minutes)
Aerobic _____
Strengthening _____
Other _____

DATE _____

Time	Food(s)	Location	Emotional state	Hunger rating
				① ② ③ ④ ⑤
				① ② ③ ④ ⑤
				① ② ③ ④ ⑤
				① ② ③ ④ ⑤
				① ② ③ ④ ⑤
				① ② ③ ④ ⑤
				① ② ③ ④ ⑤

Intake
Calories _____
Carbs _____
Fat _____
Protein _____
Activity (minutes)
Aerobic _____
Strengthening _____
Other _____

DATE _____

Time	Food(s)	Location	Emotional state	Hunger rating
				① ② ③ ④ ⑤
				① ② ③ ④ ⑤
				① ② ③ ④ ⑤
				① ② ③ ④ ⑤
				① ② ③ ④ ⑤
				① ② ③ ④ ⑤
				① ② ③ ④ ⑤

Intake
Calories _____
Carbs _____
Fat _____
Protein _____
Activity (minutes)
Aerobic _____
Strengthening _____
Other _____

MONTH _____ YEAR _____

Intake
Calories _____
Carbs _____
Fat _____
Protein _____

Activity (minutes)
Aerobic _____
Strengthening _____
Other _____

DATE _____

Time	Food(s)	Location	Emotional state	Hunger rating
				① ② ③ ④ ⑤
				① ② ③ ④ ⑤
				① ② ③ ④ ⑤
				① ② ③ ④ ⑤
				① ② ③ ④ ⑤
				① ② ③ ④ ⑤
				① ② ③ ④ ⑤

Intake
Calories _____
Carbs _____
Fat _____
Protein _____

Activity (minutes)
Aerobic _____
Strengthening _____
Other _____

DATE _____

Time	Food(s)	Location	Emotional state	Hunger rating
				① ② ③ ④ ⑤
				① ② ③ ④ ⑤
				① ② ③ ④ ⑤
				① ② ③ ④ ⑤
				① ② ③ ④ ⑤
				① ② ③ ④ ⑤
				① ② ③ ④ ⑤

Intake
Calories _____
Carbs _____
Fat _____
Protein _____

Activity (minutes)
Aerobic _____
Strengthening _____
Other _____

DATE _____

Time	Food(s)	Location	Emotional state	Hunger rating
				① ② ③ ④ ⑤
				① ② ③ ④ ⑤
				① ② ③ ④ ⑤
				① ② ③ ④ ⑤
				① ② ③ ④ ⑤
				① ② ③ ④ ⑤
				① ② ③ ④ ⑤

HOW AM I DOING?

MEASUREMENTS			WEIGHT		NOTES
	At diet's start	This month			
Chest	___ inches	___ inches	**Beginning weight** ___ pounds		_____
Upper arms	___ inches	___ inches	**This month's weight** ___ pounds		_____
Waist	___ inches	___ inches	**Total lost so far** ___ pounds		_____
Hips	___ inches	___ inches			_____
Thighs	___ inches	___ inches			_____

WEEK _____

DATE _____

Time	Food(s)	Location	Emotional state	Hunger rating
				① ② ③ ④ ⑤
				① ② ③ ④ ⑤
				① ② ③ ④ ⑤
				① ② ③ ④ ⑤
				① ② ③ ④ ⑤
				① ② ③ ④ ⑤
				① ② ③ ④ ⑤

Intake
Calories _____
Carbs _____
Fat _____
Protein _____
Activity (minutes)
Aerobic _____
Strengthening _____
Other _____

DATE _____

Time	Food(s)	Location	Emotional state	Hunger rating
				① ② ③ ④ ⑤
				① ② ③ ④ ⑤
				① ② ③ ④ ⑤
				① ② ③ ④ ⑤
				① ② ③ ④ ⑤
				① ② ③ ④ ⑤
				① ② ③ ④ ⑤

Intake
Calories _____
Carbs _____
Fat _____
Protein _____
Activity (minutes)
Aerobic _____
Strengthening _____
Other _____

DATE _____

Time	Food(s)	Location	Emotional state	Hunger rating
				① ② ③ ④ ⑤
				① ② ③ ④ ⑤
				① ② ③ ④ ⑤
				① ② ③ ④ ⑤
				① ② ③ ④ ⑤
				① ② ③ ④ ⑤
				① ② ③ ④ ⑤

Intake
Calories _____
Carbs _____
Fat _____
Protein _____
Activity (minutes)
Aerobic _____
Strengthening _____
Other _____

DATE _____

Time	Food(s)	Location	Emotional state	Hunger rating
				① ② ③ ④ ⑤
				① ② ③ ④ ⑤
				① ② ③ ④ ⑤
				① ② ③ ④ ⑤
				① ② ③ ④ ⑤
				① ② ③ ④ ⑤
				① ② ③ ④ ⑤

Intake
Calories _____
Carbs _____
Fat _____
Protein _____
Activity (minutes)
Aerobic _____
Strengthening _____
Other _____

Month _____ Year _____

Intake
Calories _____
Carbs _____
Fat _____
Protein _____

Activity (minutes)
Aerobic _____
Strengthening _____
Other _____

Date _____

Time	Food(s)	Location	Emotional state	Hunger rating
				① ② ③ ④ ⑤
				① ② ③ ④ ⑤
				① ② ③ ④ ⑤
				① ② ③ ④ ⑤
				① ② ③ ④ ⑤
				① ② ③ ④ ⑤
				① ② ③ ④ ⑤

Intake
Calories _____
Carbs _____
Fat _____
Protein _____

Activity (minutes)
Aerobic _____
Strengthening _____
Other _____

Date _____

Time	Food(s)	Location	Emotional state	Hunger rating
				① ② ③ ④ ⑤
				① ② ③ ④ ⑤
				① ② ③ ④ ⑤
				① ② ③ ④ ⑤
				① ② ③ ④ ⑤
				① ② ③ ④ ⑤
				① ② ③ ④ ⑤

Intake
Calories _____
Carbs _____
Fat _____
Protein _____

Activity (minutes)
Aerobic _____
Strengthening _____
Other _____

Date _____

Time	Food(s)	Location	Emotional state	Hunger rating
				① ② ③ ④ ⑤
				① ② ③ ④ ⑤
				① ② ③ ④ ⑤
				① ② ③ ④ ⑤
				① ② ③ ④ ⑤
				① ② ③ ④ ⑤
				① ② ③ ④ ⑤

How Am I Doing?

Weekly Weight Check

_____ pounds
_____ total lost

Tip for the Week

To jump-start your weight loss or get off a weight-loss plateau, try changing your exercise routine. If you're doing more aerobic exercise than strength training, switch your emphasis for a while. Remember, weight training builds muscle tissue, which burns more calories than fat tissue does.

☐ Done!

Date _____

Time	Food(s)	Location	Emotional state	Hunger rating
				① ② ③ ④ ⑤
				① ② ③ ④ ⑤
				① ② ③ ④ ⑤
				① ② ③ ④ ⑤
				① ② ③ ④ ⑤
				① ② ③ ④ ⑤
				① ② ③ ④ ⑤

Intake
Calories _____
Carbs _____
Fat _____
Protein _____

Activity (minutes)
Aerobic _____
Strengthening _____
Other _____

Date _____

Time	Food(s)	Location	Emotional state	Hunger rating
				① ② ③ ④ ⑤
				① ② ③ ④ ⑤
				① ② ③ ④ ⑤
				① ② ③ ④ ⑤
				① ② ③ ④ ⑤
				① ② ③ ④ ⑤
				① ② ③ ④ ⑤

Intake
Calories _____
Carbs _____
Fat _____
Protein _____

Activity (minutes)
Aerobic _____
Strengthening _____
Other _____

Date _____

Time	Food(s)	Location	Emotional state	Hunger rating
				① ② ③ ④ ⑤
				① ② ③ ④ ⑤
				① ② ③ ④ ⑤
				① ② ③ ④ ⑤
				① ② ③ ④ ⑤
				① ② ③ ④ ⑤
				① ② ③ ④ ⑤

Intake
Calories _____
Carbs _____
Fat _____
Protein _____

Activity (minutes)
Aerobic _____
Strengthening _____
Other _____

Date _____

Time	Food(s)	Location	Emotional state	Hunger rating
				① ② ③ ④ ⑤
				① ② ③ ④ ⑤
				① ② ③ ④ ⑤
				① ② ③ ④ ⑤
				① ② ③ ④ ⑤
				① ② ③ ④ ⑤
				① ② ③ ④ ⑤

Intake
Calories _____
Carbs _____
Fat _____
Protein _____

Activity (minutes)
Aerobic _____
Strengthening _____
Other _____

MONTH _____ YEAR _____

Intake
Calories _____
Carbs _____
Fat _____
Protein _____

Activity (minutes)
Aerobic _____
Strengthening _____
Other _____

DATE _____

Time	Food(s)	Location	Emotional state	Hunger rating
				① ② ③ ④ ⑤
				① ② ③ ④ ⑤
				① ② ③ ④ ⑤
				① ② ③ ④ ⑤
				① ② ③ ④ ⑤
				① ② ③ ④ ⑤
				① ② ③ ④ ⑤

Intake
Calories _____
Carbs _____
Fat _____
Protein _____

Activity (minutes)
Aerobic _____
Strengthening _____
Other _____

DATE _____

Time	Food(s)	Location	Emotional state	Hunger rating
				① ② ③ ④ ⑤
				① ② ③ ④ ⑤
				① ② ③ ④ ⑤
				① ② ③ ④ ⑤
				① ② ③ ④ ⑤
				① ② ③ ④ ⑤
				① ② ③ ④ ⑤

Intake
Calories _____
Carbs _____
Fat _____
Protein _____

Activity (minutes)
Aerobic _____
Strengthening _____
Other _____

DATE _____

Time	Food(s)	Location	Emotional state	Hunger rating
				① ② ③ ④ ⑤
				① ② ③ ④ ⑤
				① ② ③ ④ ⑤
				① ② ③ ④ ⑤
				① ② ③ ④ ⑤
				① ② ③ ④ ⑤
				① ② ③ ④ ⑤

HOW AM I DOING?

Weekly Weight Check

_____ pounds
_____ total lost

TIP FOR THE WEEK

Put smaller portions on your plate. We tend to eat the amount that's in front of us... and then some. So be careful when you serve yourself. You can always come back for more. But if you take half your normal amount the first time, even that second helping will amount to less than you usually eat.

❑ DONE!

WEEK _____

DATE _____

Time	Food(s)	Location	Emotional state	Hunger rating
				① ② ③ ④ ⑤
				① ② ③ ④ ⑤
				① ② ③ ④ ⑤
				① ② ③ ④ ⑤
				① ② ③ ④ ⑤
				① ② ③ ④ ⑤
				① ② ③ ④ ⑤

Intake
Calories _____
Carbs _____
Fat _____
Protein _____

Activity (minutes)
Aerobic _____
Strengthening _____
Other _____

DATE _____

Time	Food(s)	Location	Emotional state	Hunger rating
				① ② ③ ④ ⑤
				① ② ③ ④ ⑤
				① ② ③ ④ ⑤
				① ② ③ ④ ⑤
				① ② ③ ④ ⑤
				① ② ③ ④ ⑤
				① ② ③ ④ ⑤

Intake
Calories _____
Carbs _____
Fat _____
Protein _____

Activity (minutes)
Aerobic _____
Strengthening _____
Other _____

DATE _____

Time	Food(s)	Location	Emotional state	Hunger rating
				① ② ③ ④ ⑤
				① ② ③ ④ ⑤
				① ② ③ ④ ⑤
				① ② ③ ④ ⑤
				① ② ③ ④ ⑤
				① ② ③ ④ ⑤
				① ② ③ ④ ⑤

Intake
Calories _____
Carbs _____
Fat _____
Protein _____

Activity (minutes)
Aerobic _____
Strengthening _____
Other _____

DATE _____

Time	Food(s)	Location	Emotional state	Hunger rating
				① ② ③ ④ ⑤
				① ② ③ ④ ⑤
				① ② ③ ④ ⑤
				① ② ③ ④ ⑤
				① ② ③ ④ ⑤
				① ② ③ ④ ⑤
				① ② ③ ④ ⑤

Intake
Calories _____
Carbs _____
Fat _____
Protein _____

Activity (minutes)
Aerobic _____
Strengthening _____
Other _____

MONTH _____ YEAR _____

Intake
Calories _____
Carbs _____
Fat _____
Protein _____

Activity (minutes)
Aerobic _____
Strengthening _____
Other _____

DATE _____

Time	Food(s)	Location	Emotional state	Hunger rating
				① ② ③ ④ ⑤
				① ② ③ ④ ⑤
				① ② ③ ④ ⑤
				① ② ③ ④ ⑤
				① ② ③ ④ ⑤
				① ② ③ ④ ⑤
				① ② ③ ④ ⑤

Intake
Calories _____
Carbs _____
Fat _____
Protein _____

Activity (minutes)
Aerobic _____
Strengthening _____
Other _____

DATE _____

Time	Food(s)	Location	Emotional state	Hunger rating
				① ② ③ ④ ⑤
				① ② ③ ④ ⑤
				① ② ③ ④ ⑤
				① ② ③ ④ ⑤
				① ② ③ ④ ⑤
				① ② ③ ④ ⑤
				① ② ③ ④ ⑤

Intake
Calories _____
Carbs _____
Fat _____
Protein _____

Activity (minutes)
Aerobic _____
Strengthening _____
Other _____

DATE _____

Time	Food(s)	Location	Emotional state	Hunger rating
				① ② ③ ④ ⑤
				① ② ③ ④ ⑤
				① ② ③ ④ ⑤
				① ② ③ ④ ⑤
				① ② ③ ④ ⑤
				① ② ③ ④ ⑤
				① ② ③ ④ ⑤

HOW AM I DOING?

Weekly Weight Check

_____ pounds
_____ total lost

TIP FOR THE WEEK

Ask the waiter to give you a doggy bag along with your meal. Immediately put part of your meal in the take-home container and seal it up. Now you've got two meals for the price of one... and half the number of calories in each.

☐ DONE!

WEEK _____

DATE _____

Time	Food(s)	Location	Emotional state	Hunger rating
				① ② ③ ④ ⑤
				① ② ③ ④ ⑤
				① ② ③ ④ ⑤
				① ② ③ ④ ⑤
				① ② ③ ④ ⑤
				① ② ③ ④ ⑤
				① ② ③ ④ ⑤

Intake
Calories _____
Carbs _____
Fat _____
Protein _____
Activity (minutes)
Aerobic _____
Strengthening _____
Other _____

DATE _____

Time	Food(s)	Location	Emotional state	Hunger rating
				① ② ③ ④ ⑤
				① ② ③ ④ ⑤
				① ② ③ ④ ⑤
				① ② ③ ④ ⑤
				① ② ③ ④ ⑤
				① ② ③ ④ ⑤
				① ② ③ ④ ⑤

Intake
Calories _____
Carbs _____
Fat _____
Protein _____
Activity (minutes)
Aerobic _____
Strengthening _____
Other _____

DATE _____

Time	Food(s)	Location	Emotional state	Hunger rating
				① ② ③ ④ ⑤
				① ② ③ ④ ⑤
				① ② ③ ④ ⑤
				① ② ③ ④ ⑤
				① ② ③ ④ ⑤
				① ② ③ ④ ⑤
				① ② ③ ④ ⑤

Intake
Calories _____
Carbs _____
Fat _____
Protein _____
Activity (minutes)
Aerobic _____
Strengthening _____
Other _____

DATE _____

Time	Food(s)	Location	Emotional state	Hunger rating
				① ② ③ ④ ⑤
				① ② ③ ④ ⑤
				① ② ③ ④ ⑤
				① ② ③ ④ ⑤
				① ② ③ ④ ⑤
				① ② ③ ④ ⑤
				① ② ③ ④ ⑤

Intake
Calories _____
Carbs _____
Fat _____
Protein _____
Activity (minutes)
Aerobic _____
Strengthening _____
Other _____

MONTH _____ YEAR _____

Intake

Calories _____
Carbs _____
Fat _____
Protein _____

Activity (minutes)

Aerobic _____
Strengthening _____
Other _____

DATE _____

Time	Food(s)	Location	Emotional state	Hunger rating
				① ② ③ ④ ⑤
				① ② ③ ④ ⑤
				① ② ③ ④ ⑤
				① ② ③ ④ ⑤
				① ② ③ ④ ⑤
				① ② ③ ④ ⑤
				① ② ③ ④ ⑤

Intake

Calories _____
Carbs _____
Fat _____
Protein _____

Activity (minutes)

Aerobic _____
Strengthening _____
Other _____

DATE _____

Time	Food(s)	Location	Emotional state	Hunger rating
				① ② ③ ④ ⑤
				① ② ③ ④ ⑤
				① ② ③ ④ ⑤
				① ② ③ ④ ⑤
				① ② ③ ④ ⑤
				① ② ③ ④ ⑤
				① ② ③ ④ ⑤

Intake

Calories _____
Carbs _____
Fat _____
Protein _____

Activity (minutes)

Aerobic _____
Strengthening _____
Other _____

DATE _____

Time	Food(s)	Location	Emotional state	Hunger rating
				① ② ③ ④ ⑤
				① ② ③ ④ ⑤
				① ② ③ ④ ⑤
				① ② ③ ④ ⑤
				① ② ③ ④ ⑤
				① ② ③ ④ ⑤
				① ② ③ ④ ⑤

HOW AM I DOING?

MEASUREMENTS			WEIGHT		NOTES
	At diet's start	This month			
Chest	_____ inches	_____ inches	Beginning weight _____ pounds		_____
Upper arms	_____ inches	_____ inches	This month's weight _____ pounds		_____
Waist	_____ inches	_____ inches	Total lost so far _____ pounds		_____
Hips	_____ inches	_____ inches			_____
Thighs	_____ inches	_____ inches			_____

WEEK _____

DATE _____

Time	Food(s)	Location	Emotional state	Hunger rating
				① ② ③ ④ ⑤
				① ② ③ ④ ⑤
				① ② ③ ④ ⑤
				① ② ③ ④ ⑤
				① ② ③ ④ ⑤
				① ② ③ ④ ⑤
				① ② ③ ④ ⑤

Intake
Calories _____
Carbs _____
Fat _____
Protein _____

Activity (minutes)
Aerobic _____
Strengthening _____
Other _____

DATE _____

Time	Food(s)	Location	Emotional state	Hunger rating
				① ② ③ ④ ⑤
				① ② ③ ④ ⑤
				① ② ③ ④ ⑤
				① ② ③ ④ ⑤
				① ② ③ ④ ⑤
				① ② ③ ④ ⑤
				① ② ③ ④ ⑤

Intake
Calories _____
Carbs _____
Fat _____
Protein _____

Activity (minutes)
Aerobic _____
Strengthening _____
Other _____

DATE _____

Time	Food(s)	Location	Emotional state	Hunger rating
				① ② ③ ④ ⑤
				① ② ③ ④ ⑤
				① ② ③ ④ ⑤
				① ② ③ ④ ⑤
				① ② ③ ④ ⑤
				① ② ③ ④ ⑤
				① ② ③ ④ ⑤

Intake
Calories _____
Carbs _____
Fat _____
Protein _____

Activity (minutes)
Aerobic _____
Strengthening _____
Other _____

DATE _____

Time	Food(s)	Location	Emotional state	Hunger rating
				① ② ③ ④ ⑤
				① ② ③ ④ ⑤
				① ② ③ ④ ⑤
				① ② ③ ④ ⑤
				① ② ③ ④ ⑤
				① ② ③ ④ ⑤
				① ② ③ ④ ⑤

Intake
Calories _____
Carbs _____
Fat _____
Protein _____

Activity (minutes)
Aerobic _____
Strengthening _____
Other _____

MONTH _____ YEAR _____

Intake
Calories _____
Carbs _____
Fat _____
Protein _____
Activity (minutes)
Aerobic _____
Strengthening _____
Other _____

DATE _____

Time	Food(s)	Location	Emotional state	Hunger rating
				① ② ③ ④ ⑤
				① ② ③ ④ ⑤
				① ② ③ ④ ⑤
				① ② ③ ④ ⑤
				① ② ③ ④ ⑤
				① ② ③ ④ ⑤
				① ② ③ ④ ⑤

Intake
Calories _____
Carbs _____
Fat _____
Protein _____
Activity (minutes)
Aerobic _____
Strengthening _____
Other _____

DATE _____

Time	Food(s)	Location	Emotional state	Hunger rating
				① ② ③ ④ ⑤
				① ② ③ ④ ⑤
				① ② ③ ④ ⑤
				① ② ③ ④ ⑤
				① ② ③ ④ ⑤
				① ② ③ ④ ⑤
				① ② ③ ④ ⑤

Intake
Calories _____
Carbs _____
Fat _____
Protein _____
Activity (minutes)
Aerobic _____
Strengthening _____
Other _____

DATE _____

Time	Food(s)	Location	Emotional state	Hunger rating
				① ② ③ ④ ⑤
				① ② ③ ④ ⑤
				① ② ③ ④ ⑤
				① ② ③ ④ ⑤
				① ② ③ ④ ⑤
				① ② ③ ④ ⑤
				① ② ③ ④ ⑤

HOW AM I DOING?

Weekly Weight Check

_____ *pounds*
_____ *total lost*

TIP FOR THE WEEK

Take the time to celebrate the smaller successes.
The larger ones are sure to follow.

❏ DONE!

DATE _____

Time	Food(s)	Location	Emotional state	Hunger rating
				① ② ③ ④ ⑤
				① ② ③ ④ ⑤
				① ② ③ ④ ⑤
				① ② ③ ④ ⑤
				① ② ③ ④ ⑤
				① ② ③ ④ ⑤
				① ② ③ ④ ⑤

Intake
Calories _____
Carbs _____
Fat _____
Protein _____
Activity (minutes)
Aerobic _____
Strengthening _____
Other _____

DATE _____

Time	Food(s)	Location	Emotional state	Hunger rating
				① ② ③ ④ ⑤
				① ② ③ ④ ⑤
				① ② ③ ④ ⑤
				① ② ③ ④ ⑤
				① ② ③ ④ ⑤
				① ② ③ ④ ⑤
				① ② ③ ④ ⑤

Intake
Calories _____
Carbs _____
Fat _____
Protein _____
Activity (minutes)
Aerobic _____
Strengthening _____
Other _____

DATE _____

Time	Food(s)	Location	Emotional state	Hunger rating
				① ② ③ ④ ⑤
				① ② ③ ④ ⑤
				① ② ③ ④ ⑤
				① ② ③ ④ ⑤
				① ② ③ ④ ⑤
				① ② ③ ④ ⑤
				① ② ③ ④ ⑤

Intake
Calories _____
Carbs _____
Fat _____
Protein _____
Activity (minutes)
Aerobic _____
Strengthening _____
Other _____

DATE _____

Time	Food(s)	Location	Emotional state	Hunger rating
				① ② ③ ④ ⑤
				① ② ③ ④ ⑤
				① ② ③ ④ ⑤
				① ② ③ ④ ⑤
				① ② ③ ④ ⑤
				① ② ③ ④ ⑤
				① ② ③ ④ ⑤

Intake
Calories _____
Carbs _____
Fat _____
Protein _____
Activity (minutes)
Aerobic _____
Strengthening _____
Other _____

Intake

Calories _____
Carbs _____
Fat _____
Protein _____

Activity (minutes)

Aerobic _____
Strengthening _____
Other _____

DATE _____

Time	Food(s)	Location	Emotional state	Hunger rating
				① ② ③ ④ ⑤
				① ② ③ ④ ⑤
				① ② ③ ④ ⑤
				① ② ③ ④ ⑤
				① ② ③ ④ ⑤
				① ② ③ ④ ⑤
				① ② ③ ④ ⑤

Intake

Calories _____
Carbs _____
Fat _____
Protein _____

Activity (minutes)

Aerobic _____
Strengthening _____
Other _____

DATE _____

Time	Food(s)	Location	Emotional state	Hunger rating
				① ② ③ ④ ⑤
				① ② ③ ④ ⑤
				① ② ③ ④ ⑤
				① ② ③ ④ ⑤
				① ② ③ ④ ⑤
				① ② ③ ④ ⑤
				① ② ③ ④ ⑤

Intake

Calories _____
Carbs _____
Fat _____
Protein _____

Activity (minutes)

Aerobic _____
Strengthening _____
Other _____

DATE _____

Time	Food(s)	Location	Emotional state	Hunger rating
				① ② ③ ④ ⑤
				① ② ③ ④ ⑤
				① ② ③ ④ ⑤
				① ② ③ ④ ⑤
				① ② ③ ④ ⑤
				① ② ③ ④ ⑤
				① ② ③ ④ ⑤

HOW AM I DOING?

Weekly Weight Check

_____ pounds
_____ total lost

TIP FOR THE WEEK

Add your upper body to your aerobic exercise routine and you'll increase the number of calories you burn by as much as 10 percent.

❑ DONE!

WEEK _____

DATE _____

Time	Food(s)	Location	Emotional state	Hunger rating
				① ② ③ ④ ⑤
				① ② ③ ④ ⑤
				① ② ③ ④ ⑤
				① ② ③ ④ ⑤
				① ② ③ ④ ⑤
				① ② ③ ④ ⑤
				① ② ③ ④ ⑤

Intake
Calories _____
Carbs _____
Fat _____
Protein _____

Activity (minutes)
Aerobic _____
Strengthening _____
Other _____

DATE _____

Time	Food(s)	Location	Emotional state	Hunger rating
				① ② ③ ④ ⑤
				① ② ③ ④ ⑤
				① ② ③ ④ ⑤
				① ② ③ ④ ⑤
				① ② ③ ④ ⑤
				① ② ③ ④ ⑤
				① ② ③ ④ ⑤

Intake
Calories _____
Carbs _____
Fat _____
Protein _____

Activity (minutes)
Aerobic _____
Strengthening _____
Other _____

DATE _____

Time	Food(s)	Location	Emotional state	Hunger rating
				① ② ③ ④ ⑤
				① ② ③ ④ ⑤
				① ② ③ ④ ⑤
				① ② ③ ④ ⑤
				① ② ③ ④ ⑤
				① ② ③ ④ ⑤
				① ② ③ ④ ⑤

Intake
Calories _____
Carbs _____
Fat _____
Protein _____

Activity (minutes)
Aerobic _____
Strengthening _____
Other _____

DATE _____

Time	Food(s)	Location	Emotional state	Hunger rating
				① ② ③ ④ ⑤
				① ② ③ ④ ⑤
				① ② ③ ④ ⑤
				① ② ③ ④ ⑤
				① ② ③ ④ ⑤
				① ② ③ ④ ⑤
				① ② ③ ④ ⑤

Intake
Calories _____
Carbs _____
Fat _____
Protein _____

Activity (minutes)
Aerobic _____
Strengthening _____
Other _____

MONTH _____ YEAR _____

Intake
Calories _____
Carbs _____
Fat _____
Protein _____

Activity (minutes)
Aerobic _____
Strengthening _____
Other _____

DATE _____

Time	Food(s)	Location	Emotional state	Hunger rating
				① ② ③ ④ ⑤
				① ② ③ ④ ⑤
				① ② ③ ④ ⑤
				① ② ③ ④ ⑤
				① ② ③ ④ ⑤
				① ② ③ ④ ⑤
				① ② ③ ④ ⑤

Intake
Calories _____
Carbs _____
Fat _____
Protein _____

Activity (minutes)
Aerobic _____
Strengthening _____
Other _____

DATE _____

Time	Food(s)	Location	Emotional state	Hunger rating
				① ② ③ ④ ⑤
				① ② ③ ④ ⑤
				① ② ③ ④ ⑤
				① ② ③ ④ ⑤
				① ② ③ ④ ⑤
				① ② ③ ④ ⑤
				① ② ③ ④ ⑤

Intake
Calories _____
Carbs _____
Fat _____
Protein _____

Activity (minutes)
Aerobic _____
Strengthening _____
Other _____

DATE _____

Time	Food(s)	Location	Emotional state	Hunger rating
				① ② ③ ④ ⑤
				① ② ③ ④ ⑤
				① ② ③ ④ ⑤
				① ② ③ ④ ⑤
				① ② ③ ④ ⑤
				① ② ③ ④ ⑤
				① ② ③ ④ ⑤

HOW AM I DOING?

Weekly Weight Check

_____ *pounds*
_____ *total lost*

TIP FOR THE WEEK

Cook your pasta al dente (firm) rather than soft and mushy. Pasta that's firm is absorbed more slowly and causes less of a spike in your blood sugar.

❑ DONE!

WEEK _____

DATE _____

Time	Food(s)	Location	Emotional state	Hunger rating
				① ② ③ ④ ⑤
				① ② ③ ④ ⑤
				① ② ③ ④ ⑤
				① ② ③ ④ ⑤
				① ② ③ ④ ⑤
				① ② ③ ④ ⑤
				① ② ③ ④ ⑤

Intake
Calories _____
Carbs _____
Fat _____
Protein _____
Activity (minutes)
Aerobic _____
Strengthening _____
Other _____

DATE _____

Time	Food(s)	Location	Emotional state	Hunger rating
				① ② ③ ④ ⑤
				① ② ③ ④ ⑤
				① ② ③ ④ ⑤
				① ② ③ ④ ⑤
				① ② ③ ④ ⑤
				① ② ③ ④ ⑤
				① ② ③ ④ ⑤

Intake
Calories _____
Carbs _____
Fat _____
Protein _____
Activity (minutes)
Aerobic _____
Strengthening _____
Other _____

DATE _____

Time	Food(s)	Location	Emotional state	Hunger rating
				① ② ③ ④ ⑤
				① ② ③ ④ ⑤
				① ② ③ ④ ⑤
				① ② ③ ④ ⑤
				① ② ③ ④ ⑤
				① ② ③ ④ ⑤
				① ② ③ ④ ⑤

Intake
Calories _____
Carbs _____
Fat _____
Protein _____
Activity (minutes)
Aerobic _____
Strengthening _____
Other _____

DATE _____

Time	Food(s)	Location	Emotional state	Hunger rating
				① ② ③ ④ ⑤
				① ② ③ ④ ⑤
				① ② ③ ④ ⑤
				① ② ③ ④ ⑤
				① ② ③ ④ ⑤
				① ② ③ ④ ⑤
				① ② ③ ④ ⑤

Intake
Calories _____
Carbs _____
Fat _____
Protein _____
Activity (minutes)
Aerobic _____
Strengthening _____
Other _____

Month _____ Year _____

Intake
Calories _____
Carbs _____
Fat _____
Protein _____

Activity (minutes)
Aerobic _____
Strengthening _____
Other _____

Date _____

Time	Food(s)	Location	Emotional state	Hunger rating
				① ② ③ ④ ⑤
				① ② ③ ④ ⑤
				① ② ③ ④ ⑤
				① ② ③ ④ ⑤
				① ② ③ ④ ⑤
				① ② ③ ④ ⑤
				① ② ③ ④ ⑤

Intake
Calories _____
Carbs _____
Fat _____
Protein _____

Activity (minutes)
Aerobic _____
Strengthening _____
Other _____

Date _____

Time	Food(s)	Location	Emotional state	Hunger rating
				① ② ③ ④ ⑤
				① ② ③ ④ ⑤
				① ② ③ ④ ⑤
				① ② ③ ④ ⑤
				① ② ③ ④ ⑤
				① ② ③ ④ ⑤
				① ② ③ ④ ⑤

Intake
Calories _____
Carbs _____
Fat _____
Protein _____

Activity (minutes)
Aerobic _____
Strengthening _____
Other _____

Date _____

Time	Food(s)	Location	Emotional state	Hunger rating
				① ② ③ ④ ⑤
				① ② ③ ④ ⑤
				① ② ③ ④ ⑤
				① ② ③ ④ ⑤
				① ② ③ ④ ⑤
				① ② ③ ④ ⑤
				① ② ③ ④ ⑤

How Am I Doing?

MEASUREMENTS			WEIGHT		NOTES
	At diet's start	This month	Beginning weight	_____ pounds	_____
Chest	_____ inches	_____ inches	This month's weight	_____ pounds	_____
Upper arms	_____ inches	_____ inches	Total lost so far	_____ pounds	_____
Waist	_____ inches	_____ inches			_____
Hips	_____ inches	_____ inches			_____
Thighs	_____ inches	_____ inches			_____

DATE _____

Time	Food(s)	Location	Emotional state	Hunger rating
				① ② ③ ④ ⑤
				① ② ③ ④ ⑤
				① ② ③ ④ ⑤
				① ② ③ ④ ⑤
				① ② ③ ④ ⑤
				① ② ③ ④ ⑤
				① ② ③ ④ ⑤

Intake
Calories _____
Carbs _____
Fat _____
Protein _____
Activity (minutes)
Aerobic _____
Strengthening _____
Other _____

DATE _____

Time	Food(s)	Location	Emotional state	Hunger rating
				① ② ③ ④ ⑤
				① ② ③ ④ ⑤
				① ② ③ ④ ⑤
				① ② ③ ④ ⑤
				① ② ③ ④ ⑤
				① ② ③ ④ ⑤
				① ② ③ ④ ⑤

Intake
Calories _____
Carbs _____
Fat _____
Protein _____
Activity (minutes)
Aerobic _____
Strengthening _____
Other _____

DATE _____

Time	Food(s)	Location	Emotional state	Hunger rating
				① ② ③ ④ ⑤
				① ② ③ ④ ⑤
				① ② ③ ④ ⑤
				① ② ③ ④ ⑤
				① ② ③ ④ ⑤
				① ② ③ ④ ⑤
				① ② ③ ④ ⑤

Intake
Calories _____
Carbs _____
Fat _____
Protein _____
Activity (minutes)
Aerobic _____
Strengthening _____
Other _____

DATE _____

Time	Food(s)	Location	Emotional state	Hunger rating
				① ② ③ ④ ⑤
				① ② ③ ④ ⑤
				① ② ③ ④ ⑤
				① ② ③ ④ ⑤
				① ② ③ ④ ⑤
				① ② ③ ④ ⑤
				① ② ③ ④ ⑤

Intake
Calories _____
Carbs _____
Fat _____
Protein _____
Activity (minutes)
Aerobic _____
Strengthening _____
Other _____

MONTH _____ YEAR _____

Intake
Calories _____
Carbs _____
Fat _____
Protein _____
Activity (minutes)
Aerobic _____
Strengthening _____
Other _____

DATE _____

Time	Food(s)	Location	Emotional state	Hunger rating
				① ② ③ ④ ⑤
				① ② ③ ④ ⑤
				① ② ③ ④ ⑤
				① ② ③ ④ ⑤
				① ② ③ ④ ⑤
				① ② ③ ④ ⑤
				① ② ③ ④ ⑤

Intake
Calories _____
Carbs _____
Fat _____
Protein _____
Activity (minutes)
Aerobic _____
Strengthening _____
Other _____

DATE _____

Time	Food(s)	Location	Emotional state	Hunger rating
				① ② ③ ④ ⑤
				① ② ③ ④ ⑤
				① ② ③ ④ ⑤
				① ② ③ ④ ⑤
				① ② ③ ④ ⑤
				① ② ③ ④ ⑤
				① ② ③ ④ ⑤

Intake
Calories _____
Carbs _____
Fat _____
Protein _____
Activity (minutes)
Aerobic _____
Strengthening _____
Other _____

DATE _____

Time	Food(s)	Location	Emotional state	Hunger rating
				① ② ③ ④ ⑤
				① ② ③ ④ ⑤
				① ② ③ ④ ⑤
				① ② ③ ④ ⑤
				① ② ③ ④ ⑤
				① ② ③ ④ ⑤
				① ② ③ ④ ⑤

HOW AM I DOING?

Weekly Weight Check

_____ *pounds*
_____ *total lost*

TIP FOR THE WEEK

Break the "clean plate" habit! Always leave some food on your plate at the end of the meal. It will help prevent overeating.

❑ **DONE!**

WEEK _____

DATE _____

Time	Food(s)	Location	Emotional state	Hunger rating
				① ② ③ ④ ⑤
				① ② ③ ④ ⑤
				① ② ③ ④ ⑤
				① ② ③ ④ ⑤
				① ② ③ ④ ⑤
				① ② ③ ④ ⑤
				① ② ③ ④ ⑤

Intake

Calories _____
Carbs _____
Fat _____
Protein _____

Activity (minutes)

Aerobic _____
Strengthening _____
Other _____

DATE _____

Time	Food(s)	Location	Emotional state	Hunger rating
				① ② ③ ④ ⑤
				① ② ③ ④ ⑤
				① ② ③ ④ ⑤
				① ② ③ ④ ⑤
				① ② ③ ④ ⑤
				① ② ③ ④ ⑤
				① ② ③ ④ ⑤

Intake

Calories _____
Carbs _____
Fat _____
Protein _____

Activity (minutes)

Aerobic _____
Strengthening _____
Other _____

DATE _____

Time	Food(s)	Location	Emotional state	Hunger rating
				① ② ③ ④ ⑤
				① ② ③ ④ ⑤
				① ② ③ ④ ⑤
				① ② ③ ④ ⑤
				① ② ③ ④ ⑤
				① ② ③ ④ ⑤
				① ② ③ ④ ⑤

Intake

Calories _____
Carbs _____
Fat _____
Protein _____

Activity (minutes)

Aerobic _____
Strengthening _____
Other _____

DATE _____

Time	Food(s)	Location	Emotional state	Hunger rating
				① ② ③ ④ ⑤
				① ② ③ ④ ⑤
				① ② ③ ④ ⑤
				① ② ③ ④ ⑤
				① ② ③ ④ ⑤
				① ② ③ ④ ⑤
				① ② ③ ④ ⑤

Intake

Calories _____
Carbs _____
Fat _____
Protein _____

Activity (minutes)

Aerobic _____
Strengthening _____
Other _____

MONTH _____ YEAR _____

Intake
Calories _____
Carbs _____
Fat _____
Protein _____

Activity (minutes)
Aerobic _____
Strengthening _____
Other _____

DATE _____

Time	Food(s)	Location	Emotional state	Hunger rating
				① ② ③ ④ ⑤
				① ② ③ ④ ⑤
				① ② ③ ④ ⑤
				① ② ③ ④ ⑤
				① ② ③ ④ ⑤
				① ② ③ ④ ⑤
				① ② ③ ④ ⑤

Intake
Calories _____
Carbs _____
Fat _____
Protein _____

Activity (minutes)
Aerobic _____
Strengthening _____
Other _____

DATE _____

Time	Food(s)	Location	Emotional state	Hunger rating
				① ② ③ ④ ⑤
				① ② ③ ④ ⑤
				① ② ③ ④ ⑤
				① ② ③ ④ ⑤
				① ② ③ ④ ⑤
				① ② ③ ④ ⑤
				① ② ③ ④ ⑤

Intake
Calories _____
Carbs _____
Fat _____
Protein _____

Activity (minutes)
Aerobic _____
Strengthening _____
Other _____

DATE _____

Time	Food(s)	Location	Emotional state	Hunger rating
				① ② ③ ④ ⑤
				① ② ③ ④ ⑤
				① ② ③ ④ ⑤
				① ② ③ ④ ⑤
				① ② ③ ④ ⑤
				① ② ③ ④ ⑤
				① ② ③ ④ ⑤

HOW AM I DOING?

Weekly Weight Check

_____ pounds
_____ total lost

TIP FOR THE WEEK

It's easy to overdo it on dairy. For a quick portion-size check, visualize a pair of dice. Together they're equal to 1½ ounces of natural cheese.

☐ DONE!

WEEK _____

DATE _____

Time	Food(s)	Location	Emotional state	Hunger rating
				① ② ③ ④ ⑤
				① ② ③ ④ ⑤
				① ② ③ ④ ⑤
				① ② ③ ④ ⑤
				① ② ③ ④ ⑤
				① ② ③ ④ ⑤
				① ② ③ ④ ⑤

Intake
Calories _____
Carbs _____
Fat _____
Protein _____
Activity (minutes)
Aerobic _____
Strengthening _____
Other _____

DATE _____

Time	Food(s)	Location	Emotional state	Hunger rating
				① ② ③ ④ ⑤
				① ② ③ ④ ⑤
				① ② ③ ④ ⑤
				① ② ③ ④ ⑤
				① ② ③ ④ ⑤
				① ② ③ ④ ⑤
				① ② ③ ④ ⑤

Intake
Calories _____
Carbs _____
Fat _____
Protein _____
Activity (minutes)
Aerobic _____
Strengthening _____
Other _____

DATE _____

Time	Food(s)	Location	Emotional state	Hunger rating
				① ② ③ ④ ⑤
				① ② ③ ④ ⑤
				① ② ③ ④ ⑤
				① ② ③ ④ ⑤
				① ② ③ ④ ⑤
				① ② ③ ④ ⑤
				① ② ③ ④ ⑤

Intake
Calories _____
Carbs _____
Fat _____
Protein _____
Activity (minutes)
Aerobic _____
Strengthening _____
Other _____

DATE _____

Time	Food(s)	Location	Emotional state	Hunger rating
				① ② ③ ④ ⑤
				① ② ③ ④ ⑤
				① ② ③ ④ ⑤
				① ② ③ ④ ⑤
				① ② ③ ④ ⑤
				① ② ③ ④ ⑤
				① ② ③ ④ ⑤

Intake
Calories _____
Carbs _____
Fat _____
Protein _____
Activity (minutes)
Aerobic _____
Strengthening _____
Other _____

MONTH _____ YEAR _____

Intake
Calories _____
Carbs _____
Fat _____
Protein _____

Activity (minutes)
Aerobic _____
Strengthening _____
Other _____

DATE _____

Time	Food(s)	Location	Emotional state	Hunger rating
				① ② ③ ④ ⑤
				① ② ③ ④ ⑤
				① ② ③ ④ ⑤
				① ② ③ ④ ⑤
				① ② ③ ④ ⑤
				① ② ③ ④ ⑤
				① ② ③ ④ ⑤

Intake
Calories _____
Carbs _____
Fat _____
Protein _____

Activity (minutes)
Aerobic _____
Strengthening _____
Other _____

DATE _____

Time	Food(s)	Location	Emotional state	Hunger rating
				① ② ③ ④ ⑤
				① ② ③ ④ ⑤
				① ② ③ ④ ⑤
				① ② ③ ④ ⑤
				① ② ③ ④ ⑤
				① ② ③ ④ ⑤
				① ② ③ ④ ⑤

Intake
Calories _____
Carbs _____
Fat _____
Protein _____

Activity (minutes)
Aerobic _____
Strengthening _____
Other _____

DATE _____

Time	Food(s)	Location	Emotional state	Hunger rating
				① ② ③ ④ ⑤
				① ② ③ ④ ⑤
				① ② ③ ④ ⑤
				① ② ③ ④ ⑤
				① ② ③ ④ ⑤
				① ② ③ ④ ⑤
				① ② ③ ④ ⑤

HOW AM I DOING?

Weekly Weight Check

_____ pounds
_____ total lost

TIP FOR THE WEEK

Always extend your arms a little farther than they can reach.

❏ DONE!

WEEK _____

DATE _____

Time	Food(s)	Location	Emotional state	Hunger rating
				① ② ③ ④ ⑤
				① ② ③ ④ ⑤
				① ② ③ ④ ⑤
				① ② ③ ④ ⑤
				① ② ③ ④ ⑤
				① ② ③ ④ ⑤
				① ② ③ ④ ⑤

Intake
Calories _____
Carbs _____
Fat _____
Protein _____
Activity (minutes)
Aerobic _____
Strengthening _____
Other _____

DATE _____

Time	Food(s)	Location	Emotional state	Hunger rating
				① ② ③ ④ ⑤
				① ② ③ ④ ⑤
				① ② ③ ④ ⑤
				① ② ③ ④ ⑤
				① ② ③ ④ ⑤
				① ② ③ ④ ⑤
				① ② ③ ④ ⑤

Intake
Calories _____
Carbs _____
Fat _____
Protein _____
Activity (minutes)
Aerobic _____
Strengthening _____
Other _____

DATE _____

Time	Food(s)	Location	Emotional state	Hunger rating
				① ② ③ ④ ⑤
				① ② ③ ④ ⑤
				① ② ③ ④ ⑤
				① ② ③ ④ ⑤
				① ② ③ ④ ⑤
				① ② ③ ④ ⑤
				① ② ③ ④ ⑤

Intake
Calories _____
Carbs _____
Fat _____
Protein _____
Activity (minutes)
Aerobic _____
Strengthening _____
Other _____

DATE _____

Time	Food(s)	Location	Emotional state	Hunger rating
				① ② ③ ④ ⑤
				① ② ③ ④ ⑤
				① ② ③ ④ ⑤
				① ② ③ ④ ⑤
				① ② ③ ④ ⑤
				① ② ③ ④ ⑤
				① ② ③ ④ ⑤

Intake
Calories _____
Carbs _____
Fat _____
Protein _____
Activity (minutes)
Aerobic _____
Strengthening _____
Other _____

MONTH _____ YEAR _____

Intake
Calories _____
Carbs _____
Fat _____
Protein _____

Activity (minutes)
Aerobic _____
Strengthening _____
Other _____

DATE _____

Time	Food(s)	Location	Emotional state	Hunger rating
				① ② ③ ④ ⑤
				① ② ③ ④ ⑤
				① ② ③ ④ ⑤
				① ② ③ ④ ⑤
				① ② ③ ④ ⑤
				① ② ③ ④ ⑤
				① ② ③ ④ ⑤

Intake
Calories _____
Carbs _____
Fat _____
Protein _____

Activity (minutes)
Aerobic _____
Strengthening _____
Other _____

DATE _____

Time	Food(s)	Location	Emotional state	Hunger rating
				① ② ③ ④ ⑤
				① ② ③ ④ ⑤
				① ② ③ ④ ⑤
				① ② ③ ④ ⑤
				① ② ③ ④ ⑤
				① ② ③ ④ ⑤
				① ② ③ ④ ⑤

Intake
Calories _____
Carbs _____
Fat _____
Protein _____

Activity (minutes)
Aerobic _____
Strengthening _____
Other _____

DATE _____

Time	Food(s)	Location	Emotional state	Hunger rating
				① ② ③ ④ ⑤
				① ② ③ ④ ⑤
				① ② ③ ④ ⑤
				① ② ③ ④ ⑤
				① ② ③ ④ ⑤
				① ② ③ ④ ⑤
				① ② ③ ④ ⑤

HOW AM I DOING?

MEASUREMENTS	At diet's start	This month	WEIGHT		NOTES
Chest	_____ inches	_____ inches	Beginning weight	_____ pounds	_____
Upper arms	_____ inches	_____ inches	This month's weight	_____ pounds	_____
Waist	_____ inches	_____ inches	Total lost so far	_____ pounds	_____
Hips	_____ inches	_____ inches			_____
Thighs	_____ inches	_____ inches			_____
					_____

WEEK _____

DATE _____

Time	Food(s)	Location	Emotional state	Hunger rating
				① ② ③ ④ ⑤
				① ② ③ ④ ⑤
				① ② ③ ④ ⑤
				① ② ③ ④ ⑤
				① ② ③ ④ ⑤
				① ② ③ ④ ⑤
				① ② ③ ④ ⑤

Intake
Calories _____
Carbs _____
Fat _____
Protein _____
Activity (minutes)
Aerobic _____
Strengthening _____
Other _____

DATE _____

Time	Food(s)	Location	Emotional state	Hunger rating
				① ② ③ ④ ⑤
				① ② ③ ④ ⑤
				① ② ③ ④ ⑤
				① ② ③ ④ ⑤
				① ② ③ ④ ⑤
				① ② ③ ④ ⑤
				① ② ③ ④ ⑤

Intake
Calories _____
Carbs _____
Fat _____
Protein _____
Activity (minutes)
Aerobic _____
Strengthening _____
Other _____

DATE _____

Time	Food(s)	Location	Emotional state	Hunger rating
				① ② ③ ④ ⑤
				① ② ③ ④ ⑤
				① ② ③ ④ ⑤
				① ② ③ ④ ⑤
				① ② ③ ④ ⑤
				① ② ③ ④ ⑤
				① ② ③ ④ ⑤

Intake
Calories _____
Carbs _____
Fat _____
Protein _____
Activity (minutes)
Aerobic _____
Strengthening _____
Other _____

DATE _____

Time	Food(s)	Location	Emotional state	Hunger rating
				① ② ③ ④ ⑤
				① ② ③ ④ ⑤
				① ② ③ ④ ⑤
				① ② ③ ④ ⑤
				① ② ③ ④ ⑤
				① ② ③ ④ ⑤
				① ② ③ ④ ⑤

Intake
Calories _____
Carbs _____
Fat _____
Protein _____
Activity (minutes)
Aerobic _____
Strengthening _____
Other _____

MONTH _____ YEAR _____

Intake
Calories _____
Carbs _____
Fat _____
Protein _____

Activity (minutes)
Aerobic _____
Strengthening _____
Other _____

DATE _____

Time	Food(s)	Location	Emotional state	Hunger rating
				① ② ③ ④ ⑤
				① ② ③ ④ ⑤
				① ② ③ ④ ⑤
				① ② ③ ④ ⑤
				① ② ③ ④ ⑤
				① ② ③ ④ ⑤
				① ② ③ ④ ⑤

Intake
Calories _____
Carbs _____
Fat _____
Protein _____

Activity (minutes)
Aerobic _____
Strengthening _____
Other _____

DATE _____

Time	Food(s)	Location	Emotional state	Hunger rating
				① ② ③ ④ ⑤
				① ② ③ ④ ⑤
				① ② ③ ④ ⑤
				① ② ③ ④ ⑤
				① ② ③ ④ ⑤
				① ② ③ ④ ⑤
				① ② ③ ④ ⑤

Intake
Calories _____
Carbs _____
Fat _____
Protein _____

Activity (minutes)
Aerobic _____
Strengthening _____
Other _____

DATE _____

Time	Food(s)	Location	Emotional state	Hunger rating
				① ② ③ ④ ⑤
				① ② ③ ④ ⑤
				① ② ③ ④ ⑤
				① ② ③ ④ ⑤
				① ② ③ ④ ⑤
				① ② ③ ④ ⑤
				① ② ③ ④ ⑤

HOW AM I DOING?

Weekly Weight Check

_____ *pounds*

_____ *total lost*

TIP FOR THE WEEK

Take serving platters and bowls off the table. Leaving them there just tempts you to go for second (and third!) helpings. If the food's not readily available, you're less likely to overindulge.

❑ DONE!

DATE _____

Time	Food(s)	Location	Emotional state	Hunger rating
				① ② ③ ④ ⑤
				① ② ③ ④ ⑤
				① ② ③ ④ ⑤
				① ② ③ ④ ⑤
				① ② ③ ④ ⑤
				① ② ③ ④ ⑤
				① ② ③ ④ ⑤

Intake
Calories _____
Carbs _____
Fat _____
Protein _____

Activity (minutes)
Aerobic _____
Strengthening _____
Other _____

DATE _____

Time	Food(s)	Location	Emotional state	Hunger rating
				① ② ③ ④ ⑤
				① ② ③ ④ ⑤
				① ② ③ ④ ⑤
				① ② ③ ④ ⑤
				① ② ③ ④ ⑤
				① ② ③ ④ ⑤
				① ② ③ ④ ⑤

Intake
Calories _____
Carbs _____
Fat _____
Protein _____

Activity (minutes)
Aerobic _____
Strengthening _____
Other _____

DATE _____

Time	Food(s)	Location	Emotional state	Hunger rating
				① ② ③ ④ ⑤
				① ② ③ ④ ⑤
				① ② ③ ④ ⑤
				① ② ③ ④ ⑤
				① ② ③ ④ ⑤
				① ② ③ ④ ⑤
				① ② ③ ④ ⑤

Intake
Calories _____
Carbs _____
Fat _____
Protein _____

Activity (minutes)
Aerobic _____
Strengthening _____
Other _____

DATE _____

Time	Food(s)	Location	Emotional state	Hunger rating
				① ② ③ ④ ⑤
				① ② ③ ④ ⑤
				① ② ③ ④ ⑤
				① ② ③ ④ ⑤
				① ② ③ ④ ⑤
				① ② ③ ④ ⑤
				① ② ③ ④ ⑤

Intake
Calories _____
Carbs _____
Fat _____
Protein _____

Activity (minutes)
Aerobic _____
Strengthening _____
Other _____

MONTH _____ YEAR _____

Intake
Calories _____
Carbs _____
Fat _____
Protein _____

Activity (minutes)
Aerobic _____
Strengthening _____
Other _____

DATE _____

Time	Food(s)	Location	Emotional state	Hunger rating
				① ② ③ ④ ⑤
				① ② ③ ④ ⑤
				① ② ③ ④ ⑤
				① ② ③ ④ ⑤
				① ② ③ ④ ⑤
				① ② ③ ④ ⑤
				① ② ③ ④ ⑤

Intake
Calories _____
Carbs _____
Fat _____
Protein _____

Activity (minutes)
Aerobic _____
Strengthening _____
Other _____

DATE _____

Time	Food(s)	Location	Emotional state	Hunger rating
				① ② ③ ④ ⑤
				① ② ③ ④ ⑤
				① ② ③ ④ ⑤
				① ② ③ ④ ⑤
				① ② ③ ④ ⑤
				① ② ③ ④ ⑤
				① ② ③ ④ ⑤

Intake
Calories _____
Carbs _____
Fat _____
Protein _____

Activity (minutes)
Aerobic _____
Strengthening _____
Other _____

DATE _____

Time	Food(s)	Location	Emotional state	Hunger rating
				① ② ③ ④ ⑤
				① ② ③ ④ ⑤
				① ② ③ ④ ⑤
				① ② ③ ④ ⑤
				① ② ③ ④ ⑤
				① ② ③ ④ ⑤
				① ② ③ ④ ⑤

HOW AM I DOING?

Weekly Weight Check

_____ *pounds*

_____ *total lost*

TIP FOR THE WEEK

*Don't obsess over the number you see on the scale.
Body weight fluctuates in response to water retention
and other factors. An increase of a pound or two
may not indicate a gain of body fat.*

❑ **DONE!**

WEEK _____

DATE _____

Time	Food(s)	Location	Emotional state	Hunger rating
				① ② ③ ④ ⑤
				① ② ③ ④ ⑤
				① ② ③ ④ ⑤
				① ② ③ ④ ⑤
				① ② ③ ④ ⑤
				① ② ③ ④ ⑤
				① ② ③ ④ ⑤

Intake
Calories _____
Carbs _____
Fat _____
Protein _____

Activity (minutes)
Aerobic _____
Strengthening _____
Other _____

DATE _____

Time	Food(s)	Location	Emotional state	Hunger rating
				① ② ③ ④ ⑤
				① ② ③ ④ ⑤
				① ② ③ ④ ⑤
				① ② ③ ④ ⑤
				① ② ③ ④ ⑤
				① ② ③ ④ ⑤
				① ② ③ ④ ⑤

Intake
Calories _____
Carbs _____
Fat _____
Protein _____

Activity (minutes)
Aerobic _____
Strengthening _____
Other _____

DATE _____

Time	Food(s)	Location	Emotional state	Hunger rating
				① ② ③ ④ ⑤
				① ② ③ ④ ⑤
				① ② ③ ④ ⑤
				① ② ③ ④ ⑤
				① ② ③ ④ ⑤
				① ② ③ ④ ⑤
				① ② ③ ④ ⑤

Intake
Calories _____
Carbs _____
Fat _____
Protein _____

Activity (minutes)
Aerobic _____
Strengthening _____
Other _____

DATE _____

Time	Food(s)	Location	Emotional state	Hunger rating
				① ② ③ ④ ⑤
				① ② ③ ④ ⑤
				① ② ③ ④ ⑤
				① ② ③ ④ ⑤
				① ② ③ ④ ⑤
				① ② ③ ④ ⑤
				① ② ③ ④ ⑤

Intake
Calories _____
Carbs _____
Fat _____
Protein _____

Activity (minutes)
Aerobic _____
Strengthening _____
Other _____

MONTH _____ YEAR _____

Intake
Calories _____
Carbs _____
Fat _____
Protein _____

Activity (minutes)
Aerobic _____
Strengthening _____
Other _____

DATE _____

Time	Food(s)	Location	Emotional state	Hunger rating
				① ② ③ ④ ⑤
				① ② ③ ④ ⑤
				① ② ③ ④ ⑤
				① ② ③ ④ ⑤
				① ② ③ ④ ⑤
				① ② ③ ④ ⑤
				① ② ③ ④ ⑤

Intake
Calories _____
Carbs _____
Fat _____
Protein _____

Activity (minutes)
Aerobic _____
Strengthening _____
Other _____

DATE _____

Time	Food(s)	Location	Emotional state	Hunger rating
				① ② ③ ④ ⑤
				① ② ③ ④ ⑤
				① ② ③ ④ ⑤
				① ② ③ ④ ⑤
				① ② ③ ④ ⑤
				① ② ③ ④ ⑤
				① ② ③ ④ ⑤

Intake
Calories _____
Carbs _____
Fat _____
Protein _____

Activity (minutes)
Aerobic _____
Strengthening _____
Other _____

DATE _____

Time	Food(s)	Location	Emotional state	Hunger rating
				① ② ③ ④ ⑤
				① ② ③ ④ ⑤
				① ② ③ ④ ⑤
				① ② ③ ④ ⑤
				① ② ③ ④ ⑤
				① ② ③ ④ ⑤
				① ② ③ ④ ⑤

HOW AM I DOING?

Weekly Weight Check

_____ pounds

_____ total lost

TIP FOR THE WEEK

Don't keep "junk" foods around the house or in your drawer at work. Eating one cookie can easily lead to eating a whole row—or even the whole box. Lead yourself not into temptation!

☐ DONE!

WEEK _____

DATE _____

Time	Food(s)	Location	Emotional state	Hunger rating
				① ② ③ ④ ⑤
				① ② ③ ④ ⑤
				① ② ③ ④ ⑤
				① ② ③ ④ ⑤
				① ② ③ ④ ⑤
				① ② ③ ④ ⑤
				① ② ③ ④ ⑤

Intake
Calories _____
Carbs _____
Fat _____
Protein _____

Activity (minutes)
Aerobic _____
Strengthening _____
Other _____

DATE _____

Time	Food(s)	Location	Emotional state	Hunger rating
				① ② ③ ④ ⑤
				① ② ③ ④ ⑤
				① ② ③ ④ ⑤
				① ② ③ ④ ⑤
				① ② ③ ④ ⑤
				① ② ③ ④ ⑤
				① ② ③ ④ ⑤

Intake
Calories _____
Carbs _____
Fat _____
Protein _____

Activity (minutes)
Aerobic _____
Strengthening _____
Other _____

DATE _____

Time	Food(s)	Location	Emotional state	Hunger rating
				① ② ③ ④ ⑤
				① ② ③ ④ ⑤
				① ② ③ ④ ⑤
				① ② ③ ④ ⑤
				① ② ③ ④ ⑤
				① ② ③ ④ ⑤
				① ② ③ ④ ⑤

Intake
Calories _____
Carbs _____
Fat _____
Protein _____

Activity (minutes)
Aerobic _____
Strengthening _____
Other _____

DATE _____

Time	Food(s)	Location	Emotional state	Hunger rating
				① ② ③ ④ ⑤
				① ② ③ ④ ⑤
				① ② ③ ④ ⑤
				① ② ③ ④ ⑤
				① ② ③ ④ ⑤
				① ② ③ ④ ⑤
				① ② ③ ④ ⑤

Intake
Calories _____
Carbs _____
Fat _____
Protein _____

Activity (minutes)
Aerobic _____
Strengthening _____
Other _____

MONTH _____ YEAR _____

Intake
Calories _____
Carbs _____
Fat _____
Protein _____

Activity (minutes)
Aerobic _____
Strengthening _____
Other _____

DATE _____

Time	Food(s)	Location	Emotional state	Hunger rating
				① ② ③ ④ ⑤
				① ② ③ ④ ⑤
				① ② ③ ④ ⑤
				① ② ③ ④ ⑤
				① ② ③ ④ ⑤
				① ② ③ ④ ⑤
				① ② ③ ④ ⑤

Intake
Calories _____
Carbs _____
Fat _____
Protein _____

Activity (minutes)
Aerobic _____
Strengthening _____
Other _____

DATE _____

Time	Food(s)	Location	Emotional state	Hunger rating
				① ② ③ ④ ⑤
				① ② ③ ④ ⑤
				① ② ③ ④ ⑤
				① ② ③ ④ ⑤
				① ② ③ ④ ⑤
				① ② ③ ④ ⑤
				① ② ③ ④ ⑤

Intake
Calories _____
Carbs _____
Fat _____
Protein _____

Activity (minutes)
Aerobic _____
Strengthening _____
Other _____

DATE _____

Time	Food(s)	Location	Emotional state	Hunger rating
				① ② ③ ④ ⑤
				① ② ③ ④ ⑤
				① ② ③ ④ ⑤
				① ② ③ ④ ⑤
				① ② ③ ④ ⑤
				① ② ③ ④ ⑤
				① ② ③ ④ ⑤

HOW AM I DOING?

MEASUREMENTS	At diet's start	This month
Chest	_____ inches	_____ inches
Upper arms	_____ inches	_____ inches
Waist	_____ inches	_____ inches
Hips	_____ inches	_____ inches
Thighs	_____ inches	_____ inches

WEIGHT
Beginning weight _____ pounds
This month's weight _____ pounds
Total lost so far _____ pounds

NOTES
_____
_____
_____
_____
_____
_____

WEEK _____

DATE _____

Time	Food(s)	Location	Emotional state	Hunger rating
				① ② ③ ④ ⑤
				① ② ③ ④ ⑤
				① ② ③ ④ ⑤
				① ② ③ ④ ⑤
				① ② ③ ④ ⑤
				① ② ③ ④ ⑤
				① ② ③ ④ ⑤

Intake
Calories _____
Carbs _____
Fat _____
Protein _____
Activity (minutes)
Aerobic _____
Strengthening _____
Other _____

DATE _____

Time	Food(s)	Location	Emotional state	Hunger rating
				① ② ③ ④ ⑤
				① ② ③ ④ ⑤
				① ② ③ ④ ⑤
				① ② ③ ④ ⑤
				① ② ③ ④ ⑤
				① ② ③ ④ ⑤
				① ② ③ ④ ⑤

Intake
Calories _____
Carbs _____
Fat _____
Protein _____
Activity (minutes)
Aerobic _____
Strengthening _____
Other _____

DATE _____

Time	Food(s)	Location	Emotional state	Hunger rating
				① ② ③ ④ ⑤
				① ② ③ ④ ⑤
				① ② ③ ④ ⑤
				① ② ③ ④ ⑤
				① ② ③ ④ ⑤
				① ② ③ ④ ⑤
				① ② ③ ④ ⑤

Intake
Calories _____
Carbs _____
Fat _____
Protein _____
Activity (minutes)
Aerobic _____
Strengthening _____
Other _____

DATE _____

Time	Food(s)	Location	Emotional state	Hunger rating
				① ② ③ ④ ⑤
				① ② ③ ④ ⑤
				① ② ③ ④ ⑤
				① ② ③ ④ ⑤
				① ② ③ ④ ⑤
				① ② ③ ④ ⑤
				① ② ③ ④ ⑤

Intake
Calories _____
Carbs _____
Fat _____
Protein _____
Activity (minutes)
Aerobic _____
Strengthening _____
Other _____

MONTH _____ YEAR _____

Intake
Calories _____
Carbs _____
Fat _____
Protein _____

Activity (minutes)
Aerobic _____
Strengthening _____
Other _____

DATE _____

Time	Food(s)	Location	Emotional state	Hunger rating
				① ② ③ ④ ⑤
				① ② ③ ④ ⑤
				① ② ③ ④ ⑤
				① ② ③ ④ ⑤
				① ② ③ ④ ⑤
				① ② ③ ④ ⑤
				① ② ③ ④ ⑤

Intake
Calories _____
Carbs _____
Fat _____
Protein _____

Activity (minutes)
Aerobic _____
Strengthening _____
Other _____

DATE _____

Time	Food(s)	Location	Emotional state	Hunger rating
				① ② ③ ④ ⑤
				① ② ③ ④ ⑤
				① ② ③ ④ ⑤
				① ② ③ ④ ⑤
				① ② ③ ④ ⑤
				① ② ③ ④ ⑤
				① ② ③ ④ ⑤

Intake
Calories _____
Carbs _____
Fat _____
Protein _____

Activity (minutes)
Aerobic _____
Strengthening _____
Other _____

DATE _____

Time	Food(s)	Location	Emotional state	Hunger rating
				① ② ③ ④ ⑤
				① ② ③ ④ ⑤
				① ② ③ ④ ⑤
				① ② ③ ④ ⑤
				① ② ③ ④ ⑤
				① ② ③ ④ ⑤
				① ② ③ ④ ⑤

HOW AM I DOING?

Weekly Weight Check

_____ pounds
_____ total lost

TIP FOR THE WEEK

Minimize impulse eating by planning a weekly menu, including daily meals and snacks. Follow it and you'll avoid last-minute decisions that can derail your diet.

☐ DONE!

WEEK _____

DATE _____

Time	Food(s)	Location	Emotional state	Hunger rating
				① ② ③ ④ ⑤
				① ② ③ ④ ⑤
				① ② ③ ④ ⑤
				① ② ③ ④ ⑤
				① ② ③ ④ ⑤
				① ② ③ ④ ⑤
				① ② ③ ④ ⑤

Intake
Calories _____
Carbs _____
Fat _____
Protein _____

Activity (minutes)
Aerobic _____
Strengthening _____
Other _____

DATE _____

Time	Food(s)	Location	Emotional state	Hunger rating
				① ② ③ ④ ⑤
				① ② ③ ④ ⑤
				① ② ③ ④ ⑤
				① ② ③ ④ ⑤
				① ② ③ ④ ⑤
				① ② ③ ④ ⑤
				① ② ③ ④ ⑤

Intake
Calories _____
Carbs _____
Fat _____
Protein _____

Activity (minutes)
Aerobic _____
Strengthening _____
Other _____

DATE _____

Time	Food(s)	Location	Emotional state	Hunger rating
				① ② ③ ④ ⑤
				① ② ③ ④ ⑤
				① ② ③ ④ ⑤
				① ② ③ ④ ⑤
				① ② ③ ④ ⑤
				① ② ③ ④ ⑤
				① ② ③ ④ ⑤

Intake
Calories _____
Carbs _____
Fat _____
Protein _____

Activity (minutes)
Aerobic _____
Strengthening _____
Other _____

DATE _____

Time	Food(s)	Location	Emotional state	Hunger rating
				① ② ③ ④ ⑤
				① ② ③ ④ ⑤
				① ② ③ ④ ⑤
				① ② ③ ④ ⑤
				① ② ③ ④ ⑤
				① ② ③ ④ ⑤
				① ② ③ ④ ⑤

Intake
Calories _____
Carbs _____
Fat _____
Protein _____

Activity (minutes)
Aerobic _____
Strengthening _____
Other _____

MONTH _____ **YEAR** _____

Intake

Calories _____
Carbs _____
Fat _____
Protein _____

Activity (minutes)

Aerobic _____
Strengthening _____
Other _____

DATE _____

Time	Food(s)	Location	Emotional state	Hunger rating
				① ② ③ ④ ⑤
				① ② ③ ④ ⑤
				① ② ③ ④ ⑤
				① ② ③ ④ ⑤
				① ② ③ ④ ⑤
				① ② ③ ④ ⑤
				① ② ③ ④ ⑤

Intake

Calories _____
Carbs _____
Fat _____
Protein _____

Activity (minutes)

Aerobic _____
Strengthening _____
Other _____

DATE _____

Time	Food(s)	Location	Emotional state	Hunger rating
				① ② ③ ④ ⑤
				① ② ③ ④ ⑤
				① ② ③ ④ ⑤
				① ② ③ ④ ⑤
				① ② ③ ④ ⑤
				① ② ③ ④ ⑤
				① ② ③ ④ ⑤

Intake

Calories _____
Carbs _____
Fat _____
Protein _____

Activity (minutes)

Aerobic _____
Strengthening _____
Other _____

DATE _____

Time	Food(s)	Location	Emotional state	Hunger rating
				① ② ③ ④ ⑤
				① ② ③ ④ ⑤
				① ② ③ ④ ⑤
				① ② ③ ④ ⑤
				① ② ③ ④ ⑤
				① ② ③ ④ ⑤
				① ② ③ ④ ⑤

HOW AM I DOING?

Weekly Weight Check

_____ pounds
_____ total lost

TIP FOR THE WEEK

Try to eat mindfully, not mindlessly. Make eating an activity in itself instead of an accompaniment to watching TV or reading the paper. Savor every bite and think about what you're eating and how you feel. You'll eat less that way and enjoy it more.

☐ **DONE!**

WEEK _____

DATE _____

Time	Food(s)	Location	Emotional state	Hunger rating
				① ② ③ ④ ⑤
				① ② ③ ④ ⑤
				① ② ③ ④ ⑤
				① ② ③ ④ ⑤
				① ② ③ ④ ⑤
				① ② ③ ④ ⑤
				① ② ③ ④ ⑤

Intake
Calories _____
Carbs _____
Fat _____
Protein _____
Activity (minutes)
Aerobic _____
Strengthening _____
Other _____

DATE _____

Time	Food(s)	Location	Emotional state	Hunger rating
				① ② ③ ④ ⑤
				① ② ③ ④ ⑤
				① ② ③ ④ ⑤
				① ② ③ ④ ⑤
				① ② ③ ④ ⑤
				① ② ③ ④ ⑤
				① ② ③ ④ ⑤

Intake
Calories _____
Carbs _____
Fat _____
Protein _____
Activity (minutes)
Aerobic _____
Strengthening _____
Other _____

DATE _____

Time	Food(s)	Location	Emotional state	Hunger rating
				① ② ③ ④ ⑤
				① ② ③ ④ ⑤
				① ② ③ ④ ⑤
				① ② ③ ④ ⑤
				① ② ③ ④ ⑤
				① ② ③ ④ ⑤
				① ② ③ ④ ⑤

Intake
Calories _____
Carbs _____
Fat _____
Protein _____
Activity (minutes)
Aerobic _____
Strengthening _____
Other _____

DATE _____

Time	Food(s)	Location	Emotional state	Hunger rating
				① ② ③ ④ ⑤
				① ② ③ ④ ⑤
				① ② ③ ④ ⑤
				① ② ③ ④ ⑤
				① ② ③ ④ ⑤
				① ② ③ ④ ⑤
				① ② ③ ④ ⑤

Intake
Calories _____
Carbs _____
Fat _____
Protein _____
Activity (minutes)
Aerobic _____
Strengthening _____
Other _____

MONTH _____ YEAR _____

Intake

Calories _____
Carbs _____
Fat _____
Protein _____

Activity (minutes)

Aerobic _____
Strengthening _____
Other _____

DATE _____

Time	Food(s)	Location	Emotional state	Hunger rating
				① ② ③ ④ ⑤
				① ② ③ ④ ⑤
				① ② ③ ④ ⑤
				① ② ③ ④ ⑤
				① ② ③ ④ ⑤
				① ② ③ ④ ⑤
				① ② ③ ④ ⑤

Intake

Calories _____
Carbs _____
Fat _____
Protein _____

Activity (minutes)

Aerobic _____
Strengthening _____
Other _____

DATE _____

Time	Food(s)	Location	Emotional state	Hunger rating
				① ② ③ ④ ⑤
				① ② ③ ④ ⑤
				① ② ③ ④ ⑤
				① ② ③ ④ ⑤
				① ② ③ ④ ⑤
				① ② ③ ④ ⑤
				① ② ③ ④ ⑤

Intake

Calories _____
Carbs _____
Fat _____
Protein _____

Activity (minutes)

Aerobic _____
Strengthening _____
Other _____

DATE _____

Time	Food(s)	Location	Emotional state	Hunger rating
				① ② ③ ④ ⑤
				① ② ③ ④ ⑤
				① ② ③ ④ ⑤
				① ② ③ ④ ⑤
				① ② ③ ④ ⑤
				① ② ③ ④ ⑤
				① ② ③ ④ ⑤

HOW AM I DOING?

Weekly Weight Check

_____ pounds
_____ total lost

TIP FOR THE WEEK

Eat three meals a day. Skipping meals to cut calories will only make you feel tired, hungry, and deprived—and put you at greater risk for indulging in a weak moment.

❏ DONE!

WEEK _____

DATE _____

Time	Food(s)	Location	Emotional state	Hunger rating
				① ② ③ ④ ⑤
				① ② ③ ④ ⑤
				① ② ③ ④ ⑤
				① ② ③ ④ ⑤
				① ② ③ ④ ⑤
				① ② ③ ④ ⑤
				① ② ③ ④ ⑤

Intake
Calories _____
Carbs _____
Fat _____
Protein _____
Activity (minutes)
Aerobic _____
Strengthening _____
Other _____

DATE _____

Time	Food(s)	Location	Emotional state	Hunger rating
				① ② ③ ④ ⑤
				① ② ③ ④ ⑤
				① ② ③ ④ ⑤
				① ② ③ ④ ⑤
				① ② ③ ④ ⑤
				① ② ③ ④ ⑤
				① ② ③ ④ ⑤

Intake
Calories _____
Carbs _____
Fat _____
Protein _____
Activity (minutes)
Aerobic _____
Strengthening _____
Other _____

DATE _____

Time	Food(s)	Location	Emotional state	Hunger rating
				① ② ③ ④ ⑤
				① ② ③ ④ ⑤
				① ② ③ ④ ⑤
				① ② ③ ④ ⑤
				① ② ③ ④ ⑤
				① ② ③ ④ ⑤
				① ② ③ ④ ⑤

Intake
Calories _____
Carbs _____
Fat _____
Protein _____
Activity (minutes)
Aerobic _____
Strengthening _____
Other _____

DATE _____

Time	Food(s)	Location	Emotional state	Hunger rating
				① ② ③ ④ ⑤
				① ② ③ ④ ⑤
				① ② ③ ④ ⑤
				① ② ③ ④ ⑤
				① ② ③ ④ ⑤
				① ② ③ ④ ⑤
				① ② ③ ④ ⑤

Intake
Calories _____
Carbs _____
Fat _____
Protein _____
Activity (minutes)
Aerobic _____
Strengthening _____
Other _____

MONTH _____ YEAR _____

Intake
Calories _____
Carbs _____
Fat _____
Protein _____

Activity (minutes)
Aerobic _____
Strengthening _____
Other _____

DATE _____

Time	Food(s)	Location	Emotional state	Hunger rating
				① ② ③ ④ ⑤
				① ② ③ ④ ⑤
				① ② ③ ④ ⑤
				① ② ③ ④ ⑤
				① ② ③ ④ ⑤
				① ② ③ ④ ⑤
				① ② ③ ④ ⑤

Intake
Calories _____
Carbs _____
Fat _____
Protein _____

Activity (minutes)
Aerobic _____
Strengthening _____
Other _____

DATE _____

Time	Food(s)	Location	Emotional state	Hunger rating
				① ② ③ ④ ⑤
				① ② ③ ④ ⑤
				① ② ③ ④ ⑤
				① ② ③ ④ ⑤
				① ② ③ ④ ⑤
				① ② ③ ④ ⑤
				① ② ③ ④ ⑤

Intake
Calories _____
Carbs _____
Fat _____
Protein _____

Activity (minutes)
Aerobic _____
Strengthening _____
Other _____

DATE _____

Time	Food(s)	Location	Emotional state	Hunger rating
				① ② ③ ④ ⑤
				① ② ③ ④ ⑤
				① ② ③ ④ ⑤
				① ② ③ ④ ⑤
				① ② ③ ④ ⑤
				① ② ③ ④ ⑤
				① ② ③ ④ ⑤

HOW AM I DOING?

MEASUREMENTS			WEIGHT		NOTES
	At diet's start	This month			
Chest	_____ inches	_____ inches	Beginning weight _____ pounds		_____
Upper arms	_____ inches	_____ inches	This month's weight _____ pounds		_____
Waist	_____ inches	_____ inches	Total lost so far _____ pounds		_____
Hips	_____ inches	_____ inches			_____
Thighs	_____ inches	_____ inches			_____

The Finish Line

Date _____

My current weight _____

MY CURRENT MEASUREMENTS:

Chest	_____	inches
Upper arms	_____	inches
Waist	_____	inches
Hips	_____	inches
Thighs	_____	inches

MY CURRENT CLOTHING SIZES:

_____

_____

_____

HOW MUCH TIME AND HOW MANY DAYS I SPEND EVERY WEEK ON EXERCISE

_____ minutes _____ days a week on aerobic exercise

_____ minutes _____ days a week on strength-training exercise

MY GOALS:

To lose _____ pounds

To do aerobic exercise _____ minutes _____ days a week

To do strength-training exercise _____ minutes _____ days a week

The Nutrient Counter

Sticking to a diet means you have to choose your foods carefully. But it's not always easy to tell which foods are high in calories and low in important nutrients.

This nutrient counter will help you choose high-fiber, low-fat foods that will keep you satisfied while losing weight. The counter lists the calories and the number of grams of total carbohydrate, fiber, protein, total fat, and saturated fat in a portion. (Fiber is included in the number of grams of total carbohydrate, but the number of fiber grams is broken out so you can see how many of a food's carb grams come from this indigestible nutrient.)

Values have been rounded to the nearest whole number. "Tr" (for trace) means there's less than half a gram of that nutrient in a single portion. "NA" means the value was not available.

If you indulge in a high-calorie treat, use the counter to get back on track!

Food, portion	Cals	Total Fat (g)	Sat Fat (g)	Pro (g)	Total Carb (g)	Fiber (g)	Calc (mg)	Sod (mg)
Baked Products								
Bagel, cinnamon-raisin, 3½" dia	195	1	Tr	7	39	2	13	229
Bagel, plain (includes onion, poppy, sesame), 3½" dia	289	2	Tr	11	56	2	19	561
Biscuit, plain or buttermilk, commercially baked, 2½" dia	127	6	1	2	17	Tr	17	368

Food, portion	Cals	Total Fat (g)	Sat Fat (g)	Pro (g)	Total Carb (g)	Fiber (g)	Calc (mg)	Sod (mg)
Baked Products (cont.)								
Bread, cornbread, dry mix, prepared, 1 piece	188	6	2	4	29	1	44	467
Bread, French or Vienna (includes sourdough), 4″×2½″×1¾″	175	2	Tr	6	33	2	48	390
Bread, Italian, 1 slice	54	1	Tr	2	10	1	16	117
Bread, mixed-grain (includes whole-grain, 7-grain), 1 slice	65	1	Tr	3	12	2	24	127
Bread stick, plain, 7⅝″×⅝″	41	1	Tr	1	7	Tr	2	66
Bread stuffing, dry mix, 6 oz package	656	6	1	19	130	5	165	2703
Bread, white, 1 slice	67	1	Tr	2	13	1	38	170
Cake, chocolate, with chocolate frosting, ⅛ of 18 oz cake	235	10	3	3	35	2	28	214
Cake, pound, ⅒ of cake	116	6	3	2	15	Tr	11	119
Cheesecake, ⅙ of 17 oz cake	257	18	8	4	20	Tr	41	166
Coffeecake, fruit, ⅛ cake	156	5	1	3	26	1	23	193
Cookie, chocolate sandwich, with creme filling, 1 cookie	47	2	Tr	Tr	7	Tr	3	60
Cookies, butter, 1 cookie	23	1	1	Tr	3	Tr	1	18
Cookies, chocolate chip, soft-type, 1 cookie	69	4	1	1	9	Tr	2	49
Cookies, fig bars, 1 cookie	56	1	Tr	1	11	1	10	56
Crackers, cheese, 1 cracker, 1″ sq	5	Tr	Tr	Tr	1	Tr	2	10

Food, portion	Cals	Total Fat (g)	Sat Fat (g)	Pro (g)	Total Carb (g)	Fiber (g)	Calc (mg)	Sod (mg)
Crackers, cheese, sandwich-type with peanut butter filling, 1 sandwich	32	2	Tr	1	4	Tr	3	46
Crackers, melba toast, plain, 1 melba round	12	Tr	Tr	Tr	2	Tr	3	25
Crackers, saltines (includes oyster, soda, soup), 1 cup	195	5	1	4	32	1	54	586
Crackers, wheat, 1 cracker	9	Tr	Tr	Tr	1	Tr	1	16
Croissants, butter, 1 croissant	231	12	7	5	26	1	21	424
Croutons, seasoned, 1 cup	186	7	2	4	25	2	38	495
Danish pastry, cheese, 1 pastry	266	16	5	6	26	1	25	320
Doughnuts, cake-type, plain, sugared, or glazed, approx 3" dia	192	10	3	2	23	1	27	181
Doughnuts, yeast-leavened, glazed (includes honey buns), approx 3" dia	242	14	3	4	27	1	26	205
English muffins, plain (includes sourdough), 1 muffin	134	1	Tr	4	26	2	99	264
French toast, prepared from recipe, made with 2% milk, 1 slice	149	7	2	5	16	NA	65	311
Muffins, blueberry, 1 medium	313	7	2	6	54	3	64	505
Pancakes, buttermilk, prepared from recipe, 1 pancake, 6" dia	175	7	1	5	22	NA	121	402
Pie, apple, ⅛ of 9" dia	411	19	5	4	58	NA	11	327

Food, portion	Cals	Total Fat (g)	Sat Fat (g)	Pro (g)	Total Carb (g)	Fiber (g)	Calc (mg)	Sod (mg)
Baked Products (cont.)								
Pie, blueberry, 1/8 of 9" dia	290	13	2	2	44	1	10	406
Pita, white, 6½" dia	165	1	Tr	5	33	1	52	322
Rolls, dinner, plain, 1 oz roll	84	2	Tr	2	14	1	33	146
Rolls, dinner, whole-wheat, 1 submarine, hoagie roll	250	4	1	8	48	7	100	449
Rolls, hamburger or hot dog, plain, 1 roll	120	2	Tr	4	21	1	59	206
Taco shells, baked, approx 5" dia	62	3	Tr	1	8	1	21	49
Toaster pastries, fruit (includes apple, blueberry, cherry, strawberry), 1 pastry	204	5	1	2	37	1	14	218
Tortillas, flour, approx 6" dia	104	2	1	3	18	1	12	153
Waffles, plain, ready-to-heat (includes buttermilk), 1 waffle	95	3	Tr	2	15	1	84	284
Beef Products								
Beef, ground, 95% lean, pan-browned, 3 oz	164	6	3	25	0	0	8	72
Beef, ground, patties, frozen, broiled, medium, 3 oz	240	17	7	21	0	0	9	65
Bottom round, braised, 3 oz	181	8	3	26	0	0	4	43
Breakfast strips, cured, cooked, 3 slices	153	12	5	11	Tr	0	3	766
Brisket, whole, braised, 3 oz	247	17	6	23	0	0	6	55
Chuck, top blade, broiled, 3 oz	173	9	3	22	0	0	6	58
Eye of round, roasted, 3 oz	141	4	1	25	0	0	4	53

Food, portion	Cals	Total Fat (g)	Sat Fat (g)	Pro (g)	Total Carb (g)	Fiber (g)	Calc (mg)	Sod (mg)
Rib, eye, broiled, 3 oz	174	8	3	25	0	0	14	51
Rib, prime, broiled, 3 oz	250	18	8	21	0	0	7	60
Short loin, porterhouse steak, broiled, 3 oz	235	16	6	20	0	0	6	55
Short loin, T-bone steak, broiled, 3 oz	168	8	3	22	0	0	3	60
Tenderloin, broiled, 3 oz	175	8	0	25	0	0	14	50
BEVERAGES								
Beer, light, 12 fl oz	99	0	0	1	5	0	18	11
Beer, regular, 12 fl oz	117	Tr	0	1	6	Tr	18	14
Carbonated beverage, low calorie, other than cola or pepper, no caffeine, 12 fl oz	0	0	0	Tr	0	0	14	21
Chocolate syrup, 2 tbsp	109	Tr	Tr	1	25	1	5	28
Cola, carbonated, 12 fl oz	155	0	0	Tr	40	0	11	15
Cranberry juice cocktail, bottled, 8 fl oz	144	Tr	Tr	0	36	Tr	8	5
Ginger ale, carbonated, 12 fl oz	124	0	0	0	32	0	11	26
Grape juice drink, canned, 8 fl oz	125	0	0	Tr	32	0	8	3
KOOL-AID Tropical Punch, sweetened, powder, 1 serving	64	0	0	0	16	0	28	2
Lemonade, frozen concentrate, white, prepared with water, 8 fl oz	131	Tr	Tr	Tr	34	Tr	10	7
NESTEA Iced Tea, Lemon Flavor, ready-to-drink, 8 fl oz	89	1	Tr	0	20	0	NA	0

Food, portion	Cals	Total Fat (g)	Sat Fat (g)	Pro (g)	Total Carb (g)	Fiber (g)	Calc (mg)	Sod (mg)
Beverages (cont.)								
Orange juice drink, 8 fl oz	132	0	0	Tr	33	0	5	5
Pineapple and grapefruit juice drink, canned, 8 fl oz	118	Tr	Tr	1	29	Tr	18	35
RICE DREAM, canned, 8 fl oz	120	2	Tr	Tr	25	0	20	86
Shake, chocolate, 8 fl oz	211	6	4	6	34	3	188	161
Wine, table, red, 1 glass, 3.5 fl oz	74	0	0	Tr	2	0	8	5
Wine, table, white, 1 glass, 3.5 fl oz	70	0	0	Tr	1	0	9	5
Breakfast Cereals								
CHEERIOS, 1 cup	111	2	Tr	3	22	3	100	273
CORN FLAKES, 1 cup	101	Tr	Tr	2	24	1	2	203
CREAM OF RICE, cooked with water, 1 cup	127	Tr	Tr	2	28	Tr	7	2
CREAM OF WHEAT, instant, prepared with water, 1 cup	149	1	Tr	4	32	1	154	10
FIBER ONE, ½ cup	59	1	Tr	2	24	14	100	129
FROSTED FLAKES, ¾ cup	114	Tr	Tr	1	28	1	2	148
HONEY BUNCHES OF OATS, ¾ cup	118	2	Tr	2	25	1	6	193
Multi-Bran CHEX, 1 cup	166	1	Tr	3	41	6	89	322
POST 100% BRAN Cereal, ⅓ cup	83	1	Tr	4	23	8	22	121
POST GRAPE-NUTS, ½ cup	208	1	Tr	6	47	5	20	354
PRODUCT 19, 1 cup	100	Tr	Tr	2	25	1	5	207

FOOD, PORTION	CALS	TOTAL FAT (G)	SAT FAT (G)	PRO (G)	TOTAL CARB (G)	FIBER (G)	CALC (MG)	SOD (MG)
QUAKER Instant Oatmeal, apples and cinnamon, 1 packet, prepared	130	1	Tr	3	26	3	110	165
RAISIN BRAN, 1 cup	195	2	Tr	5	47	7	29	362
RICE KRISPIES, 1¼ cups	119	Tr	Tr	2	29	Tr	5	319
WHEATIES, 1 cup	107	1	Tr	3	24	3	0	218
Whole Grain TOTAL, ¾ cup	97	1	Tr	2	23	2	1000	192
CEREAL GRAINS AND PASTA								
Barley, 1 cup	651	4	1	23	135	32	61	22
Couscous, cooked, 1 cup	176	Tr	Tr	6	36	2	13	8
Macaroni, cooked, enriched, 1 cup small shells	162	1	Tr	5	33	1	8	1
Noodles, egg, cooked, enriched, 1 cup	213	2	Tr	8	40	2	19	11
Pasta, fresh-refrigerated, plain, cooked, 2 oz	75	1	Tr	3	14	NA	3	3
Rice, brown, long-grain, cooked, 1 cup	216	2	Tr	5	45	4	20	10
Rice noodles, cooked, 1 cup	192	Tr	Tr	2	44	2	7	33
Rice, white, cooked, 1 cup	169	Tr	Tr	4	37	2	3	9
Spaghetti, cooked, enriched, 1 cup	197	1	Tr	7	40	2	10	1
Wheat flour, white, 1 cup	455	1	Tr	13	95	3	19	3
Wheat flour, whole-grain, 1 cup	407	2	Tr	16	87	15	41	6
Wild rice, cooked, 1 cup	166	1	Tr	7	35	3	5	5
DAIRY AND EGG PRODUCTS								
Butter, salted, 1 tbsp	102	12	6	Tr	Tr	0	3	82

Food, portion	Cals	Total Fat (g)	Sat Fat (g)	Pro (g)	Total Carb (g)	Fiber (g)	Calc (mg)	Sod (mg)
Dairy and Egg Products (cont.)								
Cheese, American, 1 oz	94	7	4	6	2	0	141	274
Cheese, cheddar, 1 slice	113	9	6	7	Tr	0	202	174
Cheese, cream, 1 tbsp	51	5	3	1	Tr	0	12	43
Cheese, mozzarella, part skim milk, 1 oz	72	5	3	7	1	0	222	175
Cheese, parmesan, grated, 1 cup	431	29	17	38	4	0	1109	1529
CHEEZ WHIZ, 2 tbsp	91	7	4	4	3	Tr	118	541
Cottage cheese, 2% milkfat, 1 cup	203	4	3	31	8	0	156	918
Cream, half-and-half, 1 fl oz	39	3	2	1	1	0	32	12
Cream, sour, reduced fat, 1 tbsp	20	2	1	Tr	1	0	16	6
Egg substitute, liquid, 1 cup	211	8	2	30	2	0	133	444
Egg, whole, hard-boiled, 1 large	78	5	2	6	1	0	25	62
Egg, whole, scrambled, 1 large	101	7	2	7	1	0	43	171
Milk, 2%, 1 cup	122	5	2	8	11	0	271	115
Milk, whole, 1 cup	146	8	5	8	11	0	246	105
Milk, nonfat, 1 cup	83	Tr	Tr	8	12	0	223	108
Yogurt, fruit, nonfat, 8 oz	213	Tr	Tr	10	43	0	345	132
Yogurt, vanilla, low fat, 8 oz	193	3	2	11	31	0	388	150
Fast Foods								
Biscuit with egg and sausage, 1 biscuit	581	39	15	19	41	1	155	1141

FOOD, PORTION	CALS	TOTAL FAT (G)	SAT FAT (G)	PRO (G)	TOTAL CARB (G)	FIBER (G)	CALC (MG)	SOD (MG)
Burrito, with beans, cheese, and beef, 2 pieces	331	13	7	15	40	NA	130	991
Cheeseburger, large, single patty, with condiments and vegetables, 1 sandwich	563	33	15	28	38	NA	206	1108
Chicken, breaded and fried, boneless, 6 pieces	319	21	5	18	15	NA	14	513
Chicken, breaded and fried, light meat (breast or wing), 2 pieces	494	30	8	36	20	NA	60	975
Chicken fillet sandwich, plain, 1 sandwich	515	29	9	24	39	NA	60	957
Coleslaw, ¾ cup	147	11	2	1	13	NA	34	267
Fish fillet, battered or breaded, fried, 1 fillet	211	11	3	13	15	Tr	16	484
Fish sandwich, with tartar sauce, 1 sandwich	431	23	5	17	41	NA	84	615
French toast with butter, 2 slices	356	19	8	10	36	NA	73	513
Hamburger, single patty, with condiments, 1 sandwich	427	21	8	23	37	2	134	731
Hot dog, plain, 1 sandwich	242	15	5	10	18	NA	24	670
Nachos, with cheese, 6–8 nachos	346	19	8	9	36	NA	272	816
Pizza with pepperoni, 1 slice	181	7	2	10	20	NA	65	267
Potato, baked, with cheese sauce and broccoli, 1 piece	403	21	9	14	47	NA	336	485
Potato, french fried in vegetable oil, 1 medium	458	25	5	6	53	5	19	265

Food, portion	Cals	Total Fat (g)	Sat Fat (g)	Pro (g)	Total Carb (g)	Fiber (g)	Calc (mg)	Sod (mg)
Fast Foods (cont.)								
Potato salad, ⅓ cup	108	6	1	1	13	NA	13	312
Roast beef sandwich, plain, 1 sandwich	346	14	4	22	33	NA	54	792
Salad, vegetable, tossed, without dressing, with chicken, 1½ cups	105	2	1	17	4	NA	37	209
Salad, vegetable, tossed, without dressing, with pasta and seafood, 1½ cups	379	21	3	16	32	NA	71	1572
Shrimp, breaded and fried, 6–8 shrimp	454	25	5	19	40	NA	84	1446
Submarine sandwich, with cold cuts	456	19	7	22	51	NA	189	1651
Taco, 1 large	568	32	17	32	41	NA	339	1233
Fats and Oils								
Lard, 1 tbsp	115	13	5	0	0	0	0	0
Margarine, 80% fat, stick, 1 tbsp	99	11	2	Tr	Tr	0	Tr	92
Margarine spread, fat-free, tub, 1 tbsp	6	Tr	Tr	Tr	1	0	1	85
Margarine, spread, soybean, 1 tbsp	87	10	2	Tr	Tr	NA	1	98
Mayonnaise dressing, no cholesterol, 1 tbsp	103	12	2	0	Tr	0	1	73
MIRACLE WHIP FREE, nonfat, 1 tbsp	13	Tr	Tr	Tr	2	Tr	1	126
Oil, corn and canola, 1 tbsp	124	14	1	0	0	0	0	0
Oil, olive, 1 tbsp	119	14	2	0	0	0	Tr	Tr
Oil, soybean, 1 tbsp	120	14	2	0	0	0	0	0

Food, portion	Cals	Total Fat (g)	Sat Fat (g)	Pro (g)	Total Carb (g)	Fiber (g)	Calc (mg)	Sod (mg)
Salad dressing, French, 1 tbsp	73	7	1	Tr	2	0	4	134
Salad dressing, Italian, 1 tbsp	43	4	1	Tr	2	0	1	243
Salad dressing, thousand island, 1 tbsp	59	6	1	Tr	2	Tr	3	138
FINFISH AND SHELLFISH PRODUCTS								
Catfish, breaded and fried, 3 oz	195	11	3	15	7	1	37	238
Cod, Atlantic, cooked, dry heat, 3 oz	89	1	Tr	19	0	0	12	66
Crab, Alaska king, cooked, moist heat, 1 leg	130	2	Tr	26	0	0	79	1436
Fish sticks, frozen, preheated, 1 stick	76	3	1	4	7	Tr	6	163
Lobster, northern, cooked, 3 oz	83	1	Tr	17	1	0	52	323
Ocean perch, cooked, dry heat, 3 oz	103	2	Tr	20	0	0	116	82
Roughy, orange, cooked, dry heat, 3 oz	76	1	Tr	16	0	0	32	69
Salmon, Atlantic, farmed, cooked, 3 oz	175	10	2	19	0	0	13	52
Sardine, Atlantic, canned in oil, drained solids with bone, 2 sardines	50	3	Tr	6	0	0	92	121
Scallop, breaded and fried, 2 large	67	3	1	6	3	NA	13	144
Shrimp, mixed, breaded and fried, 3 oz	206	10	2	18	10	Tr	57	292

FOOD, PORTION	CALS	TOTAL FAT (G)	SAT FAT (G)	PRO (G)	TOTAL CARB (G)	FIBER (G)	CALC (MG)	SOD (MG)
FINFISH AND SHELLFISH PRODUCTS (CONT.)								
Shrimp, mixed, cooked, moist heat, 3 oz	84	1	Tr	18	0	0	33	190
Snapper, mixed, cooked, dry heat, 3 oz	109	1	Tr	22	0	0	34	48
Surimi, 3 oz	84	1	Tr	13	6	0	8	122
Trout, rainbow, wild, cooked, dry heat, 3 oz	128	5	1	19	0	0	73	48
Tuna, light, canned in water, drained, 1 can	191	1	Tr	42	0	0	18	558
FRUITS AND FRUIT JUICES								
Apple juice, canned or bottled, unsweetened, 1 cup	117	Tr	Tr	Tr	29	Tr	17	7
Apples, raw, with skin, 2¾" dia	72	Tr	Tr	Tr	19	3	8	1
Applesauce, canned, sweetened, 1 cup	194	Tr	Tr	Tr	51	3	10	8
Bananas, raw, 1 medium	105	Tr	Tr	1	27	3	6	1
Blueberries, raw, 1 cup	83	Tr	Tr	1	21	3	9	1
Cantaloupe, raw, 1 wedge, ⅛ of melon	35	Tr	Tr	1	8	1	9	16
Cherries, sweet, raw, 1 cup, with pits	74	Tr	Tr	1	19	2	15	0
Cranberries, raw, 1 cup, whole	44	Tr	Tr	Tr	12	4	8	2
Cranberry juice, unsweetened, 1 cup	116	Tr	Tr	1	31	Tr	20	5
Cranberry sauce, canned, sweetened, 1 cup	418	Tr	Tr	1	108	3	11	80

Food, portion	Cals	Total Fat (g)	Sat Fat (g)	Pro (g)	Total Carb (g)	Fiber (g)	Calc (mg)	Sod (mg)
Fruit cocktail juice pack, 1 cup	109	Tr	Tr	1	28	2	19	9
Grapefruit juice, white, canned, sweetened, 1 cup	115	Tr	Tr	1	28	Tr	20	5
Grapefruit, raw, pink and red, ½ fruit, 3¾" dia	37	Tr	Tr	1	9	1	18	0
Grapes, red or green, raw, 1 grape, seedless	3	Tr	Tr	Tr	1	Tr	1	Tr
Honeydew, ⅛ of a melon	45	Tr	Tr	1	11	1	8	23
Kiwi fruit, skinless, 1 fruit	56	Tr	Tr	1	13	3	31	3
Mangos, raw, 1 fruit	135	1	Tr	1	35	4	21	4
Nectarines, raw, 1 fruit, 2½" dia	60	Tr	Tr	1	14	2	8	0
Olives, ripe, canned, 1 large	5	Tr	Tr	Tr	Tr	Tr	4	38
Orange juice, 1 cup	112	Tr	Tr	2	26	Tr	27	2
Oranges, raw, 1 fruit, 2⅝" dia	62	Tr	Tr	1	15	3	52	0
Peaches, canned, juice pack, 1 cup, halves or slices	109	Tr	Tr	2	29	3	15	10
Peaches, raw, 2½" dia	38	Tr	Tr	1	9	1	6	0
Pears, raw, 2½ per lb	96	Tr	Tr	1	26	5	15	2
Pineapple, canned, juice pack, drained, 1 cup, chunks	109	Tr	Tr	1	28	2	29	2
Pineapple juice, canned, unsweetened, 1 cup	140	Tr	Tr	1	34	1	43	3
Plums, raw, 1 fruit, 2⅛" dia	30	Tr	Tr	Tr	8	1	4	0
Prunes, uncooked, 1 cup, pitted	408	1	Tr	4	109	12	73	3

Food, portion	Cals	Total Fat (g)	Sat Fat (g)	Pro (g)	Total Carb (g)	Fiber (g)	Calc (mg)	Sod (mg)
Fruits and Fruit Juices (cont.)								
Raisins, seedless, .5 oz	42	Tr	Tr	Tr	11	1	7	2
Strawberries, raw, 1 cup	46	Tr	Tr	1	11	3	23	1
Tangerines (mandarin oranges), raw, 1 medium	37	Tr	Tr	1	9	2	12	1
Watermelon, 1/16 of melon	86	Tr	Tr	2	22	1	20	3
Lamb and Veal								
Lamb, ground, broiled, 3 oz	241	17	7	21	0	0	19	69
Lamb, leg, (shank and sirloin), roasted, 3 oz	162	7	3	23	0	0	8	61
Veal, loin, roasted, 3 oz	184	10	4	21	0	0	16	79
Veal, rib, braised, 3 oz	185	7	2	29	0	0	20	84
Veal, sirloin, braised, 3 oz	214	11	4	27	0	0	14	67
Legumes and Legume Products								
Bacon bits, meatless, 1 tbsp	33	2	Tr	2	2	1	7	124
Beans, baked, canned, 1 cup	236	1	Tr	12	52	13	127	1008
Beans, black, boiled, 1 cup	227	1	Tr	15	41	15	46	2
Beans, kidney, red, boiled, 1 cup	225	1	Tr	15	40	13	50	4
Beans, navy, boiled, 1 cup	258	1	Tr	16	48	12	127	2
Chili with beans, canned, 1 cup	287	14	6	15	30	11	120	1336
Cowpeas (blackeyes, crowder, southern), boiled, 1 cup	200	1	Tr	13	36	11	41	7
Falafel, home-prepared, 1 patty, 2 1/4" dia	57	3	Tr	2	5	NA	9	50
Hummus, commercial, 1 cup	415	24	4	20	36	15	95	948

FOOD, PORTION	CALS	TOTAL FAT (G)	SAT FAT (G)	PRO (G)	TOTAL CARB (G)	FIBER (G)	CALC (MG)	SOD (MG)
Lentils, boiled, 1 cup	230	1	Tr	18	40	16	38	4
Lima beans, boiled, 1 cup	216	1	Tr	15	39	13	32	4
MORI-NU, Tofu, silken, soft, 1 slice	46	2	Tr	4	2	Tr	26	4
Peanut butter, smooth style, with salt, 2 tbsp	192	17	3	8	6	2	15	160
Peanuts, dry-roasted, without salt, 1 cup	854	73	10	35	31	12	79	9
Peas, split, boiled, 1 cup	231	1	Tr	16	41	16	27	4
Refried beans, canned, 1 cup	237	3	1	14	39	13	88	753
Soy milk, 1 cup	120	5	1	9	11	3	10	29
Soy sauce, soy and wheat (shoyu), 1 tbsp	8	Tr	Tr	1	1	Tr	3	914
Soyburger, 1 patty	125	4	1	13	9	3	20	385

MEALS, ENTRÉES, AND SIDEDISHES

FOOD, PORTION	CALS	TOTAL FAT (G)	SAT FAT (G)	PRO (G)	TOTAL CARB (G)	FIBER (G)	CALC (MG)	SOD (MG)
BANQUET Turkey & Gravy with Dressing Meal, frozen meal, 1 serving	280	10	3	14	34	3	47	1061
Beef stew, canned, 1 serving	218	12	5	11	16	3	28	947
CHEF BOYARDEE Spaghetti & Meatballs in Tomato Sauce, 1 serving	250	9	4	9	34	2	17	941
CHUN KING Sweet & Sour Vegetables & Sauce with Chicken, canned, 1 serving	165	2	0	6	32	NA	NA	564
GREEN GIANT, Broccoli in Cheese Flavored Sauce, frozen, 1 serving	75	3	1	3	10	NA	NA	538

Food, portion	Cals	Total Fat (g)	Sat Fat (g)	Pro (g)	Total Carb (g)	Fiber (g)	Calc (mg)	Sod (mg)
Meals, Entrées, and Sidedishes (cont.)								
HEALTHY CHOICE Chicken Teriyaki with Rice Medley, frozen, 1 serving	268	6	3	17	37	3	37	602
HOT POCKETS Ham 'N Cheese, frozen, 1 serving	340	14	6	15	38	NA	251	666
KRAFT Macaroni and Cheese Dinner Original Flavor, unprepared, 1 serving	259	3	1	11	48	1	92	561
LIPTON, Alfredo Egg Noodles in a Creamy Sauce, dry mix, 1 serving	259	7	3	10	39	NA	79	1097
MARIE CALLENDER'S Escalloped Noodles & Chicken, frozen, 1 cup	397	21	7	13	38	NA	104	1007
OLD EL PASO Chili with Beans, 1 serving	249	10	2	18	22	10	NA	588
STOUFFER'S, Creamed Spinach, frozen, 1 serving	169	13	4	4	9	2	141	335
THE BUDGET GOURMET Italian Sausage Lasagna, frozen, 1 serving	456	24	8	21	40	3	316	903
Tortellini, pasta with cheese filling, ¾ cup	249	6	3	11	38	2	123	279
TYSON Chicken Fajita Kit, frozen, 1 serving	129	3	1	8	17	0	0	350
Nut and Seed Products								
Almonds, 1 cup, whole	827	72	6	30	28	17	355	1
Mixed nuts, peanuts, dry roasted, salt added, 1 cup	814	70	9	24	35	12	96	917
Pecans, 1 cup, halves	684	71	6	9	14	10	69	0

Food, portion	Cals	Total Fat (g)	Sat Fat (g)	Pro (g)	Total Carb (g)	Fiber (g)	Calc (mg)	Sod (mg)
Pistachio nuts, dry roasted, salt added, 1 cup	699	57	7	26	33	13	135	498
Sunflower seed kernels, dried, 1 cup	821	71	7	33	27	15	167	4
Walnuts, English, 1 cup, ground	523	52	5	12	11	5	78	2
PORK PRODUCTS								
Bacon, cured, pan-fried, 1 slice cooked	42	3	1	3	Tr	0	1	192
Canadian-style bacon, cured, grilled, 2 slices	87	4	1	11	1	0	5	727
Ham, boneless, (11% fat), roasted, 3 oz	151	8	3	19	0	0	7	1275
Ham, leg, shank half, roasted, 3 oz	246	17	6	22	0	0	13	50
Pork, fresh, ground, cooked, 3 oz	252	18	7	22	0	0	19	62
Pork, sirloin (chops), boneless, braised, 3 oz	149	6	2	23	0	0	11	39
Pork, tenderloin, roasted, 3 oz	147	5	2	24	0	0	5	47
POULTRY PRODUCTS								
Chicken, breast, meat and skin, batter-fried, ½ breast, bone removed	364	18	5	35	13	Tr	28	385
Chicken, drumstick, meat and skin, batter-fried, 1 drumstick, bone removed	193	11	3	16	6	Tr	12	194
Chicken, leg, meat and skin, roasted, 1 leg, bone removed	264	15	4	30	0	0	14	99

Food, portion	Cals	Total Fat (g)	Sat Fat (g)	Pro (g)	Total Carb (g)	Fiber (g)	Calc (mg)	Sod (mg)
Poultry Products (cont.)								
Chicken wing, meat and skin, batter-fried, 1 wing, bone removed	159	11	3	10	5	Tr	10	157
Cornish game hens, meat and skin, roasted, 1 bird	668	47	13	57	0	0	33	164
Ground turkey, cooked, 4 oz patty	193	11	3	22	0	0	21	88
Turkey, breast, meat and skin, roasted, ½ breast, bone removed	1633	64	18	248	0	0	181	544
Turkey, leg, meat and skin, roasted, 1 leg	148	7	2	20	0	0	23	55
Turkey, wing, meat and skin, roasted, 1 wing, bone removed	426	23	6	51	0	0	45	113
Sausages and Luncheon Meats								
Beef, cured, pastrami, 1 oz	98	8	3	5	1	0	3	344
Beef, sausage, smoked, 1 sausage	134	12	5	6	1	0	3	486
Bologna, beef, 1 serving	87	8	3	3	1	0	9	302
Bologna, turkey, 1 serving	59	4	1	3	1	Tr	34	351
Chicken breast, oven-roasted, fat-free, sliced, 1 serving	33	Tr	Tr	7	1	0	3	452
Frankfurter, beef, 5" long×¾" in dia	149	13	5	5	2	0	6	513
Ham, sliced, regular (11% fat), 1 slice	46	2	1	5	1	Tr	7	365
Pepperoni, pork, beef, 1 oz	130	11	5	6	1	Tr	6	501

Food, portion	Cals	Total Fat (g)	Sat Fat (g)	Pro (g)	Total Carb (g)	Fiber (g)	Calc (mg)	Sod (mg)
Salami, cooked, beef, 1 slice	67	6	3	3	Tr	0	2	296
Sausage, Italian, pork, cooked, 1 link	268	21	8	17	1	0	20	765
Turkey sausage, reduced fat, brown and serve, 1 cup	256	13	4	22	14	Tr	40	790

SNACKS

Food, portion	Cals	Total Fat (g)	Sat Fat (g)	Pro (g)	Total Carb (g)	Fiber (g)	Calc (mg)	Sod (mg)
Beef jerky, chopped and formed, 1 piece	82	5	2	7	2	Tr	4	443
Cheese puffs and twists, low fat, 1 oz	122	3	1	2	21	3	101	364
Granola bars, soft, uncoated, chocolate chip, 1 bar	118	5	3	2	19	1	26	76
Popcorn, air-popped, 1 cup	31	Tr	Tr	1	6	1	1	Tr
Potato chips, barbecue-flavor, 1 bag, 7 oz	972	64	16	15	105	9	99	1485
Potato chips, made from dried potatoes, plain, 1 can, 7 oz	1105	76	19	12	101	7	48	1299
Pretzels, hard, plain, unsalted, 10 twists	229	2	Tr	5	48	2	22	173
Pretzels, soft, 1 medium	389	4	1	9	80	2	26	1615
Puffs or twists, corn-based, extruded, cheese-flavor, 1 bag, 8 oz	1258	78	15	17	122	2	132	2384
Rice cake, cracker, 1 cubic inch	16	Tr	Tr	Tr	3	Tr	Tr	3
Sesame sticks, wheat-based, salted, 1 oz	153	10	2	3	13	1	48	422

Food, portion	Cals	Total Fat (g)	Sat Fat (g)	Pro (g)	Total Carb (g)	Fiber (g)	Calc (mg)	Sod (mg)
Snacks (cont.)								
Tortilla chips, plain, 1 oz	142	7	1	2	18	2	44	150
Trail mix, with chocolate chips, salted nuts, and seeds, 1 cup	707	47	9	21	66	NA	159	177
Soups, Sauces, and Gravies								
Barbecue sauce, 1 cup (8 fl oz)	188	5	1	5	32	3	48	2038
Gravy, beef, canned, 1 cup	123	5	3	9	11	1	14	1305
Sauce, pasta, spaghetti/marinara, ready-to-serve, 1 cup	143	5	1	4	21	4	55	1030
Soup, black bean, canned, prepared with equal volume water, 1 cup	116	2	Tr	6	20	4	44	1198
Soup, chicken noodle, canned, prepared with equal volume water, 1 cup	75	2	1	4	9	1	17	1106
Soup, cream of chicken, prepared with equal volume milk, 1 cup	191	11	5	7	15	Tr	181	1047
Soup, pea, green, canned, prepared with equal volume milk, 1 cup	239	7	4	13	32	3	173	970
Soup, tomato, canned, prepared with equal volume water, 1 cup	85	2	Tr	2	17	Tr	12	695
Soup, vegetarian vegetable, canned, prepared with equal volume water, 1 cup	72	2	Tr	2	12	Tr	22	822

FOOD, PORTION	CALS	TOTAL FAT (G)	SAT FAT (G)	PRO (G)	TOTAL CARB (G)	FIBER (G)	CALC (MG)	SOD (MG)
SWEETS								
3 MUSKETEERS Bar, 1 bar, 1.81 oz	212	7	3	2	39	1	43	99
ALMOND JOY Candy Bar, 1 package, 1.76 oz	235	13	9	2	29	2	31	70
BABY RUTH Bar, 1 bar, 0.75 oz	97	5	3	1	13	1	9	45
Caramels, 1 piece	39	1	1	Tr	8	Tr	14	25
Frozen yogurts, chocolate, 1 cup	221	6	4	5	38	4	174	110
Fruit and juice bars, 1 bar, 2.5 fl oz	63	Tr	0	1	16	1	4	3
Gumdrops, starch jelly, 10 gummy bears	87	0	0	0	22	Tr	1	10
Honey, 1 tbsp	64	0	0	Tr	17	Tr	1	1
Ice creams, vanilla, ½ cup	145	8	5	3	17	1	92	58
Jams and preserves, 1 tbsp	56	Tr	Tr	Tr	14	Tr	4	6
Jellybeans, 10 pieces	105	Tr	0	0	26	Tr	1	14
KIT KAT BIG KAT Bar, 1 bar, 1.94 oz	286	15	10	3	35	1	76	35
"M&M's" Milk Chocolate Candies, 1 package, 1.69 oz	236	10	6	2	34	1	50	29
Marshmallows, 1 regular	23	Tr	Tr	Tr	6	Tr	Tr	6
MILKY WAY Bar, 1 bar, 1.9 oz	228	9	4	2	39	1	70	130
MR. GOODBAR Chocolate Bar, 1 bar, 1.75 oz	264	16	7	5	27	2	54	20
Puddings, chocolate, ready-to-eat, 5 oz	197	6	1	4	33	1	128	183

Food, portion	Cals	Total Fat (g)	Sat Fat (g)	Pro (g)	Total Carb (g)	Fiber (g)	Calc (mg)	Sod (mg)
Sweets (cont.)								
RAISINETS Chocolate Covered Raisins, 1 package, 1.58 oz	185	7	3	2	32	2	49	16
Sherbet, orange, 1 bar, 2.75 fl oz	95	1	1	1	20	2	36	30
SKITTLES Bite Size Candies, 1 package, 2 oz	231	2	Tr	Tr	52	0	0	9
SNICKERS Bar, 1 bar, 2 oz	273	14	5	5	34	1	54	152
Sugars, granulated, 1 tsp	16	0	0	0	4	0	Tr	0
Syrups, chocolate, fudge-type, 2 tbsp	133	3	2	2	24	1	38	131
Syrups, table blends, pancake, 1 tbsp	47	0	0	0	12	Tr	1	16
TWIZZLERS Strawberry Twists Candy, 4 pieces	133	1	0	1	30	0	0	109
YORK Peppermint Pattie, 1 patty, 1.5 oz	165	3	2	1	35	1	5	12
Vegetables and Vegetable Products								
Artichoke, boiled, with salt, 1 artichoke	60	Tr	Tr	4	13	6	54	397
Asparagus, frozen, boiled, with salt, 1 cup	32	1	Tr	5	3	3	32	432
Beans, lima, canned, solids and liquids, ½ cup	88	Tr	Tr	5	17	4	35	312
Beans, snap, green, boiled, drained, 1 cup	44	Tr	Tr	2	10	4	55	1
Broccoli, chopped, boiled, drained, ½ cup	27	Tr	Tr	2	6	3	31	32
Carrots, raw, 1 medium	25	Tr	Tr	1	6	2	20	42

FOOD, PORTION	CALS	TOTAL FAT (G)	SAT FAT (G)	PRO (G)	TOTAL CARB (G)	FIBER (G)	CALC (MG)	SOD (MG)
Catsup, 1 tbsp	14	Tr	Tr	Tr	4	Tr	3	167
Cauliflower, boiled, drained, ½ cup	14	Tr	Tr	1	3	2	10	9
Celery, diced, raw, 1 cup	17	Tr	Tr	1	4	2	48	96
Corn, sweet, yellow, canned, cream style, 1 cup	184	1	Tr	4	46	3	8	8
Corn, sweet, yellow, raw, 1 ear	123	2	Tr	5	27	4	3	21
Cucumber, sliced, peeled, raw, 1 cup	14	Tr	Tr	1	3	1	17	2
Mustard greens, boiled, drained, 1 cup	21	Tr	Tr	3	3	3	104	22
Okra, sliced, boiled, drained, ½ cup	18	Tr	Tr	1	4	2	62	5
Onion rings, breaded, frozen, heated in oven, 10 rings, 2–3" dia	244	16	5	3	23	1	19	225
Onions, raw, 1 slice, thin	4	Tr	Tr	Tr	1	Tr	2	Tr
Peas, green, canned, seasoned, solids and liquids, 1 cup	114	1	Tr	7	21	5	34	577
Peppers, sweet, green, raw, 1 pepper	24	Tr	Tr	1	6	2	12	4
Peppers, sweet, red, raw, 1 pepper	31	Tr	Tr	1	7	2	8	2
Pickle, cucumber, sweet, 1 slice	8	Tr	Tr	Tr	2	Tr	Tr	66
Pickles, cucumber, dill, 1 slice	1	Tr	Tr	Tr	Tr	Tr	1	90
Potato, baked, flesh and skin, 1 medium	161	Tr	Tr	4	37	4	26	17

Food, portion	Cals	Total Fat (g)	Sat Fat (g)	Pro (g)	Total Carb (g)	Fiber (g)	Calc (mg)	Sod (mg)
Vegetables and Vegetable Products (cont.)								
Potatoes, french fried, frozen, heated in oven, with salt, 10 strips	100	4	1	2	16	2	4	133
Potatoes, hashed brown, home-prepared, 1 cup	413	20	2	5	55	5	22	534
Potatoes, white, flesh and skin, baked, 1 medium	163	Tr	Tr	4	36	4	17	12
Spinach, frozen, chopped or leaf, boiled, drained, ½ cup	30	Tr	Tr	4	5	4	145	92
Sweet potato, cooked, baked in skin, 1 medium	103	Tr	Tr	2	24	4	43	41
Sweet potato, cooked, candied, home-prepared, 1 piece, 2½"×2" dia	144	3	1	1	29	3	27	74
Tomato juice, canned, 1 fl oz	5	Tr	Tr	Tr	1	Tr	3	3
Tomato paste, canned, with salt added, 6 oz can	139	1	Tr	7	32	8	61	1343
Tomato sauce, canned, with mushrooms, 1 cup	86	Tr	Tr	4	21	4	32	1107
Tomatoes, red, raw, 1 cup	38	1	Tr	2	8	2	9	16
Tomatoes, sun-dried, 1 cup	139	2	Tr	8	30	7	59	1131
Vegetable juice cocktail, canned, 1 cup	46	Tr	Tr	2	11	2	27	653
Yam, cubed, boiled, drained, or baked, 1 cup	158	Tr	Tr	2	38	5	19	11
Zucchini, baby, raw, 1 medium	2	Tr	Tr	Tr	Tr	Tr	2	Tr
Zucchini, with skin, frozen boiled, drained, 1 cup	38	Tr	Tr	3	8	3	38	4